THE LEES OF ARLINGTON

The Story of Mary and Robert E. Lee

Mary Custis Lee and Robert E. Lee

THE LEES OF ARLINGTON

The Story of Mary and Robert E. Lee

By MARGUERITE VANCE

Illustrated by Nedda Walker

THE JUNIOR LITERARY GUILD

and

E. P. DUTTON & COMPANY, INC.

NEW YORK

2136

For

MARGARET VANCE PASCOE

CONTENTS

ACKNOWLEDGMENT

Acknowledgment is made to the following for help in preparing the manuscript.

RECOLLECTIONS AND PRIVATE MEMOIRS OF WASHINGTON
By his adopted son, George Washington Parke Custis, with a memoir of the author by his daughter, Mary Anne Randolph Custis Lee.
Derby & Jackson, 1860

MRS. ROBERT E. LEE
Rose Mortimer E. MacDonald
Ginn and Company, 1939

THE LEE MANSION
Randle Bond Truett
Hastings House, 1943

RECOLLECTIONS AND LETTERS OF ROBERT E. LEE
Captain Robert E. Lee
Doubleday, 1904

MARSE ROBERT, KNIGHT OF·THE CONFEDERACY
James C. Young
Henkle, 1929

PERSONAL REMINISCENCES OF ROBERT E. LEE
By the Reverend J. William Jones
Appleton, 1874

ROBERT E. LEE (Vols. 1 & 2)
Douglas Southall Freeman
Charles Scribners Sons, 1934-5

SPRINGTIME IN VIRGINIA
Samuel Chamberlain
Hastings House, 1947

THE RAVEN: A BIOGRAPHY OF SAM HOUSTON
Marquis James
Bobbs Merrill, 1929

ROBERT E. LEE: A BIOGRAPHY
Robert W. Winston
William Morrow & Co., 1934

HOMES AND GARDENS IN OLD VIRGINIA
Edited by Susanne Williams Massie & Frances Archer Christian
J. W. Ferguson & Sons. Richmond, Va.

THE LEES OF VIRGINIA
Burton J. Hendrick
Little Brown, 1935

THAT COUNTRY CALLED VIRGINIA
Lena Barksdale
Alfred Knopf, 1945

NELLY CUSTIS, DAUGHTER OF MOUNT VERNON
Rose Mortimer E. MacDonald
Ginn and Company, 1937

ROBERT E. LEE AND THE SOUTHERN CONFEDERACY, 1807-1870
H. A. White
Putnam, 1897

ROBERT E. LEE
W. Wilson
University of North Carolina Press, 1924

THE LEES OF ARLINGTON

The Story of Mary and Robert E. Lee

Chapter 1

NOT CRYING OVER FRECKLES, MARY?

THE road leading from Alexandria to *Arlington* streamed out along the river like a strip of clay-colored homespun measuring tape, stretched there by a careful hand to compute the short distance that separated the thriving town from the Custis estate, today the site of Arlington National Cemetery.

The well oiled, sparkling wheels of the big landeau rolled silently except when a bit of shale or rock ground briefly against them. Only the brisk, measured beat of hoofs and the pleasant jingle of bit chains broke the late afternoon quiet. Overhead, little clouds like puffs of cotton fresh-picked from the boll, moved lazily across the sky and were reflected in the river. The day had been almost unbearably hot but now a slight breeze seemed moving up from the Chesapeake and the air was suddenly sweet with the smell of kelp and nicotine flower.

It was, thought Mary Custis, an enchanting time to be driving back home from Alexandria like this in an open carriage, seated across from Mama and Papa, with no further need to watch your manners every second or to curtsy and look properly pleased when some very, very old gentlemen would pat your shoulder and say: "Upon my word, Patsy Dandridge over again — except for size, my dear, except for size. Patsy was a tiny thing. You're a tall gel, Miss Mary, tall like the Fitzhughs."

Mary clenched the fingers of one hand in its lace mitt in the palm of the other as they lay folded in her lap and leaned back. The movement pushed her perky little hat with its shaded green plumes down over her forehead and she left it there while she kept her eyes on the road unwinding in the wake of the carriage.

Patsy Dandridge — Gracious, Great-Grandmamma had even had a romantic name when she was a belle at *Chestnut Grove* on the Pamunkey River. Not enough that she was tiny and pretty and had pink cheeks, but she must needs have a name which seemed to come straight out of a romance! Patsy Dandridge. Everyone, just *everyone* talked about how lovely she had been at Governor Gooch's ball — people who perhaps had not actually seen her but had heard about her from their parents or grandparents; of how dainty and twinkling her every gesture and movement had been, and of how Daniel Parke Custis had lost his heart completely. Oh, me! (Mary sighed and pushed her hat back but it promptly settled over her forehead again) So they were married and lived — no, not quite happily ever after. At the end of only eight years, little Great-Grandmamma was a widow with two children, Jackie a toddler and Patty, a tiny baby to share the big, lonely plantation, *The White House,* a few miles up the Pamunkey from *Chestnut Grove.*

Then, (Mary particularly loved this part of the story) the handsome young Colonial officer, hero of the French and Indian wars, Colonel George Washington, had come a-riding. There was a wedding on Twelfth Night, with festivities that lasted a week. Soon Colonel and Mrs. Washington went to *Mount Vernon* to live, taking the two Custis children with them.

Great-Grandmamma must have been wonderfully happy during the years at *Mount Vernon.* Colonel Washington loved her so dearly and showered her and the children with every luxury money could buy; and the children could not have been treated with more tender care if they had been his own. But frail little Patty died when she was only sixteen, and Jackie, when little more than a boy himself, married Eleanor Calvert and moved to a home of his own.

(A soft mist drifted across the fields and from the woods rose the bitter-sweet smell of moss and rotting bark and of damp earth that seldom feels the sun's warmth. Mary shivered.)

A few years later the war had come, the American Revolution, and Colonel Washington became General Washington, Commander-in-Chief of the American army. For eight heartbreaking years he led the Colonies in their fight against the stupid monarch of England, the motherland. In the end there was victory and the United States of America was an established, independent nation. And Jackie Custis, the last of Great-Grandmamma's children, lay dead of trench fever at *Eltham Hall,* not far from *The White House* where he was born.

Great-Grandmamma and General Washington took Eleanor and Jackie's youngest two children, Nelly and little George Washington Parke Custis, to *Mount Vernon* to live. (Mary twisted a delicate gold-and-enamel bracelet on her wrist. Her brows puckered as they always did when she was deep in thought and her mouth tilted its corners in a dreamy smile. Aunt Nelly Lewis who lived down the river at *Woodlawn,* had given her the bracelet.) it was always hard to think of Aunt Nelly and Papa as having been those two little children at *Mount Vernon* so long ago. As far back as she could remember, Mary had loved to think of that fact in all its enchanting facets: the little boy romping with his baby sister and their nurse on the broad lawn sloping down to the river; the lad at school; the young poet who much preferred writing verses to studying Virgil; the meeting with popular, sixteen-year-old Mary Lee Fitzhugh — Mama; and now the happy life at *Arlington*. Oh, me, it was all so exciting, so romantic!

"Mary child, are you listening?"

Mary caught herself up sharply. Daydreaming had its drawbacks; it was apt to render one deaf and blind to one's surroundings. Mama, beautiful and romantic herself, was sure to understand and to make allowances, but Papa had no patience whatever with inattention.

"Oh, yes, Papa. I mean no, Papa." Mary's cheeks were scarlet. She sat erect and her feather bobbed. "I'm sorry, Papa," she stammered. "I was thinking about Great-Grandmamma and the General and. . . ." Her voice trailed off and she reached up nervously to tuck back a wisp of hair that blew out from under her hat and looked hopefully at her mother.

Mrs. Custis smiled. Though Mary had the rather long nose and pointed chin of the Custises, it was from her mother that she had inherited her graceful stature and flawless skin and soft, fair hair. The Fitzhugh women were all noted for their beauty, their tall, slender grace. And Mary's twinkling sense of humor was a gift from her mother, too, a sense of humor that set her dimpling and chuckling when every staid drop of Custis blood in her veins admonished: "Careful, Mary, careful. This is no time for levity."

"Papa's Fourth of July speech may well have made you think of the *Mount Vernon* family, dear," the mother comforted, "but now Papa has asked you a question." Her voice carried encouragement and it would have taken a much sterner man than George Washington Parke Custis to withstand the half pleading smile which his wife directed at him from under her drooping Leghorn. "We all were very proud," she added and repeated, "*very* proud indeed."

The effect of her words was exactly as she had hoped. Mr. Custis beamed. "You liked the speech then, Mary Lee?" he questioned. "I confess that speaking in the Masonic Hall at Alexandria always fills me with the greatest nervousness. The acoustics are bad and it is infuriating to drive home a point with all the eloquence at your command only to have it come echoing back at you ten seconds later like a jeer."

He removed his tall, cream-colored beaver for a moment and mopped his brow and head with an enormous, white silk handkerchief. "What I was remarking, Mary child, while you were daydreaming," he continued, settling the hat again carefully, "was that it struck me young Rob Lee is shooting up like a wild cucumber. But the lad's too solemn, too much of a sobersides. Why, how old is that boy? Sixteen or seventeen or thereabouts? Now at his age, let me see, hm, about that time young George Washington de Lafayette was in this country and the General — only by that time we called him the President — had invited him to *Mount Vernon*. I remember Lafayette's father, too, but dimly. He visited us when your Aunt Nelly and I were mere babies and we watched him plant the magnolia tree which still stands in the *Mount Vernon* garden. But young Lafayette — *what* a time we had! From all up and down the Potomac, boys and girls about our age came swarming. We had boating parties and barbecues; we danced the Virginia Reel and tore across country on paper chases and played every silly game invented. . . ."

"And never studied a lesson," his wife interrupted. "Ah, Nelly's told me many and many a time, so don't deny it." She patted his knee, laughing mischievously at him, and Mary facing them, wondered at the good fortune that had made her the daughter of such dear parents. But her father was speaking again, this time to his wife.

"Right you are, Mary Lee, right you are, my dear," he admitted, smiling ruefully at Mrs. Custis, "and no one feels more strongly than I do that diligence in study is, hm, most important. Still, young Robert today looked as harassed as some of our own congressmen. The lad's too young to wear such a grim expression. What frets him so, Mary? There was quite a gathering of you young people around the refreshment table after the, hm, hm, speech, yet I noticed that Robert alone seemed not to be cutting capers with the other young rapscallions. What do they say of such a dignified boy? Ah, here we are, here we are, to be sure. Good to be home."

The landeau turned in at the gates of *Arlington* and rolled to a stop before its impressive portico. Mary's answer must wait. In her heart she knew it probably never would be given. Papa's interest in so relatively unimportant a subject as a boy's dejection was sure to be short lived. Now, if it had been something like the clever turn of a phrase or the choice of color used by an artist in the painting of a sunset, why, then Papa could be counted on to cling to the subject for hours on end, as indeed he often did.

Like colored prisms settling into patterned designs in a kaleidescope, these thoughts jockeyed about in Mary's mind as she followed her mother up the shallow steps and crossed the dim, cool portico. Was she, she wondered in guilty panic, being disloyal to Papa, dear, kind, generous Papa? No, of course not. Only Mama seemed always to understand and to be interested in other people's problems. Papa, on the other hand, appeared to be more interested in having people understand *his* problem, *his* point of view. Ah, well, Mary reflected, gentlemen had so many more problems than ladies, after all. Undoubtedly Papa was right.

She caught a glimpse of herself in a tall mirror as she began mounting the stairs to her room and sighed. In her long, narrow, short-waisted frock and plumed hat she decided she was painfully thin. Blond curls straggled across her shoulders; her eyes, so dark under their thick lashes

and delicately arching brows as to challenge one to name their color, were deep blue. Their expression was whimsical, as though laughter lay forever in their depths, ready to sparkle forth with the first up-curving of Mary's lips. Laughter came easily to Mary Randolph Custis, though never in ridicule and very often at herself.

Now she hesitated a moment on the bottom step and studied the frail looking girl who gazed back at her from the mirror. Then deliberately she made a face. "I do declare, Mary Custis," she whispered, "the old gentlemen were right when they said you were 'a tall gel.' You're a down-right bean pole and thin as a shad, and you have freckles, millions of them — nothing to call a smile from — well, any lad. And pretty little Portia Hodgeson, all dimples and round, pink cheeks, had Robert Lee laughing, actually *laughing,* mind you!"

Mary walked slowly upstairs, her thoughts back in the rose garden at *Ravensworth,* her uncle William Fitz-hugh's estate, where only a little more than a month ago, Robert had seemed to find what she said interesting enough even though laughter had played no part in it.

Mrs. Custis had preceded her upstairs and Mary could hear her in conversation with her maid as she laid aside her bonnet. Mr. Custis was enjoying himself with a book in a corner of his favorite settle on the portico. Late sunshine lay in broad bands across the brick floor; still light enough for a chapter or hm, hm, two. A discrete tinkle of silver and china in the dining room and the smell of frying chicken drifting up from the summer kitchen hinted at supper time. Suddenly Mary lifted her long skirts and ran up the remaining stairs.

"Mama," she said a little breathlessly, leaning in the doorway of Mrs. Custis's room, "if I drink milk and eat worlds of fried chicken and grits and biscuit and — and — floating island, do you think, well, do you think that maybe I might gain some weight? I looked in the glass just now and I — I'm a very scarecrow!"

Her voice broke and tears began sliding down her cheeks. In an agony of embarrassment, for Mary seldom cried, she buried her face in her hands and wheeled about to leave the room. But Mrs. Custis stopped her. Swiftly she crossed to her side and put her arms around the silently weeping girl.

"Darling — darling child," she comforted, drawing Mary's head to her shoulder and smoothing the fair hair, "what nonsense is this? 'Scarecrow'! Who or what put such an idea into your head? Remember, dear, people form their estimates of us from the estimates we in turn place upon ourselves. Scarecrow, indeed!"

"But I'm so thin, Mama, and I h-h-have s-s-so many f-f-f-freckles!" The words tumbled after one another in a stuttering torrent of sobs. Here was grief, poignant, devastating as grief can only be to a girl whose seventeenth birthday is but three months away.

Her mother was puzzled and her heart ached for this beloved only child who until now had shown no interest whatever in her appearance. Young for her age, Mary always had been a happy fly-away who tried the patience of everyone who hoped to make her stand still long enough to fit a frock or to experiment with a new hair arrangement. In a day when girls of sixteen took endless precautions against sunburn and tan, Mary ran bare-headed across the sunny lawns of *Arlington* in spite of admonitions and warnings. By mid-summer her fair skin was generously sprayed with freckles and her naturally golden hair was bleached to the color of straw. But if she was conscious of all this, certainly she gave it little thought. Now, suddenly out of the blue, tears and frantic plans for improvement.

Mrs. Custis smiled quietly as she patted the still heaving shoulder. Could it be that at last a bit of natural feminine vanity was making itself felt in Mary who had scoffed at it for so long?

"Hush, dear," she said. "Stop crying or your eyes will be swollen at supper and Papa will wonder. Freckles aren't anything to get into a state over. Buttermilk and cucumbers will take care of them in no time. Yes, really," as Mary stirred and partly raised her head. "As for being thin, it's true I'd be happy if you weighed a little more, but only because more weight would give you more strength. Of all the pretty girls I saw in Alexandria this afternoon, none was prettier or sweeter than my Mary!

"They say — listen, dear. Here ——" she pushed a handkerchief gently between the hot cheek and the fingers cupped over it——"they say Great-Grandmamma at your age fretted exactly as you are fretting now, but because she felt she was far too plump and much too short. Only they tell me Great-Grandmamma wasted little time on tears. She'd too much spunk for that. She was a very great lady and knew more than her share of sorrow, but one of her best-known characteristics, one that helped to make and to *keep* her the great lady she was, was her *spunk*. Martha Washington never was known to shed tears or brood over what could not be helped. Remember that, darling. You're her great-grandchild."

Mary blew her nose and lifted her head to smile obliquely at her mother. "I'm sorry, Mama," she said. "I didn't mean to be such a silly Susan. I'll have spunk, too. Great-Grandmamma would be every proud of me. Just wait and see."

Chapter II

YOUNGER SON

MEANWHILE, what of "young Rob Lee" whose solemnity had roused such concern in Mr. Custis that Fourth of July afternoon in 1823?

Robert Lee hurried along through the dappled sunshine of late afternoon, his cheeks flushed, the wavy black hair clinging in moist wisps against his brow. He carried his hat and as he moved swiftly down the street he slapped at shrubs and gate posts in a kind of gay hail and farewell. He was a tall boy, slim and straight, with the blackest hair imaginable and dark eyes which even in his youth held a brooding tenderness when they looked on small or hurt or helpless things.

A certain loftiness of bearing, a certain imperious tilt of the head bespoke the generations of proud Carter and Lee ancestors from whom he had sprung. And if this young son of Virginia lacked an aptitude for easy laughter, there was a reason which perhaps he never suspected.

*   *   *   *

Stratford Hall in Westmorland County, Virginia, was a bleak forbidding structure full of legends and ghosts of another era. Its great hall was draughty and on a blustery January morning in 1807 from one of the rooms on the main floor came the wavering cry of a newborn child.

Ann Carter Lee looked down at the tiny dark head on her arm and drew the blanket closer. Another son. Carter, her first-born, was nine; little Anne seven; Smith five. Now here was the baby brother Anne had prayed for nightly. Anne would be ecstatic. If only ———. Suddenly the room swam in a green-and-gold glitter and the mother closed her eyes against rising tears.

Surely no girl could have dreamed of a more gallant, more dashing suitor than Henry Lee, distinguished soldier of the American Revolution. Added to this, was not the romantic cavalier who came galloping up the broad avenue to *Shirley* the Carter plantation mansion, Governor of Virginia as well? Seventeen years older than pretty Ann Hill Carter to be sure and a widower, and a man not entirely trusted by her father, yet who ever had been able to resist the charm of "Light Horse Harry" Lee?

So they were married at beautiful *Shirley* on a June evening in 1793 and for a few years Ann's happiness seemed to refute her father's skepticism. If grim, fortress-like *Stratford Hall* on the Potomac was depressing after *Shirley,* serenely facing the James, Ann took comfort in the knowledge that *Stratford Hall* need not always be her home. When her husband's son by a former marriage came of age, *Stratford Hall* would be his. Then she and Henry could go to a newer, brighter home of their own. That there could be even the slightest doubt of this never entered the young wife's mind.

But now the predictions of Ann's father began to bear bitter fruit. Henry Lee's third term as Governor came to an end. For one term he was a member of Congress where his sole achievement seems to have been his famous speech praising George Washington as "first in war, first in peace, first in the hearts of his countrymen."

"Light Horse Harry" began speculating, investing large sums of money in business schemes to make still more money — quickly. When these plans failed and his own resources ran low he borrowed, then borrowed again. At last nothing remained of his fortune or of the vast sums he had borrowed, and Lee suffered the humiliation of being sent to debtors' prison for more than a year.

There were four little children at *Stratford Hall* now and the gentle mother who had dreamed so happily of the day when she and her husband would leave the gloomy place, suddenly realized with a sinking heart that now she had no choice; she *must* leave. Her stepson had reached his majority; *Stratford Hall* was his; she and her husband and their children were his guests. Ann Lee's proud spirit rebelled.

In the trim little city of Alexandria on the Virginia side of the Potomac, she found a comfortable if unpretentious brick house and to it she and Henry Lee moved with their brood. Their sole income now was in the form of revenue from a trust fund left Ann by her father. On it they could manage to live, but that was all. Scarcely were they settled in the new home when another baby, a little girl, was born and was named Mildred. Robert was five.

The war of 1812 had broken out. Great Britain was again our enemy. Not everyone agreed with President Madison that a war was necessary and among these people was a young Baltimore editor named Alexander C. Hanson. Articles in his paper did not please most Americans. Henry Lee, however, admired his courage and, finding himself in Baltimore on a day when mob violence broke out around Hanson's printing plant, he went to his aid. Lee was wounded and terribly disfigured, his fine spirit broken, his career ended. Sick and penniless, he left for the West Indies, never to return.

To little Robert Lee his father had always been a hero and an idol. Now, bewildered at the tearful leave-taking, at the pall of tragedy and insecurity that hung over the little house on Cameron Street, the boy felt strangely alone. Something he knew must be very, very wrong, else why were they here with only a city back yard to play in instead of the spreading acres of *Stratford Hall* to romp over? (Though he had been only a toddler when they had left Westmorland County, the memory of the plantation was indelibly fixed in his mind.) Why had the people hurt Papa so? Why had he gone away? and where? Why did Mama cry when she thought no one was watching? These were some of the questions that tormented the serious, dark-eyed little boy. Unconsciously he drew nearer his mother, not for protection but to protect her against forces which he could not understand.

So the years slipped by. Careful investments made it possible for Ann Lee to move her family to a somewhat more pretentious house at the corner of Princess and Washington Streets. Carter, now eighteen, entered Harvard. Smith, too, was away at school. Mildred was a sunny-haired little girl of four; Robert was nine and growing tall. Anne ——

On a cold, rainy evening in 1815, Robert and Anne bent over an enormous book of fine engravings. Mama had given Robert permission to get it from the big case to look at, providing Anne turned the pages. Between the sixteen-year-old girl and her brother, seven years younger, there was a bond of affection and understanding which was to endure even through the terrible war years when he had become the idol of the Confederacy and she was the wife of a Union sympathizer. He was her prayed-for baby brother; she was his "Annie."

Robert brought the book which smelled pleasantly of Morocco leather, from the library and laid it carefully on the dining room table. Then he stood back, all rapt attention, waiting for the first page to turn. Anne reached behind her and drew up a chair and sat down. Robert found he could see better by standing and Anne drew him to her, her left hand, palm down on the table, her right hand beginning to turn the pages. Completely absorbed, Robert shifted his position a little, his chin in his cupped hand, his elbow resting all unconsciously on the top of Anne's left hand. An hour passed as the two pored over the beautiful plates. Then it was bedtime and Robert unwillingly struggled back to reality. He lifted his head.

"Can't we look at just . . . just two more pictures?" he coaxed. "It's only half pa ———." His voice stuck in his throat and all thought of what he had wanted to say vanished like steam from a windowpane when a sudden draught of cold wind blows across it. Frozen with horror, he looked at Anne.

She sat rigid, her face the color of putty, staring at her hand which still lay, palm down on the table. Her lips twitched as she tried to smile, but to Robert the poor effort was a grimace and his Annie a stranger.

"I — I can't move it, Robbie," she whispered, trying to keep her lips steady. "Don't be frightened, just call Mammy or Nat or someone — please — quick."

As Robert stumbled from the room he heard a soft rustle behind him. Anne had slumped forward, face down across the great book.

In the kitchen, Nat, the butler-coachman was drying the supper dishes for Lula, his wife, who was the cook. Suddenly the dining room door flew open and Robert stood there, his chest heaving as though he had been running in a gale, his eyes dark wells of terror as he motioned wordlessly behind him.

"Mas' Rob, what's wrong?" Nat's towel dropped with a damp thud on the table. Lula rubbed soapy palms down the length of her apron, then together they dashed by the frightened boy.

Anne was carried, unconscious, to bed and Nat ran for the doctor who came presently, rain dripping from his hat brim. Examination showed nothing more than a small bruise on Anne's hand, but the fingers remained cramped and the slightest contact, even a sheet brushing against the bruised hand, caused excruciating pain. Mystified, the doctor administered a sedative, then questioned Nat and Lula. Their stories told him nothing. Mrs. Lee, who had been lying on the couch in her room reading when the accident occurred, could offer no clue as she bent anxiously over the suffering girl. Finally the good doctor decided to question Robert.

"Tell us what happened, Son," the kindly man coaxed, drawing Robert to him and looking into the rigid little face.

"Nothing happened, sir," the boy reiterated earnestly. "We were looking at pictures and when Annie said it was bedtime and we closed the book she — she looked all white and — sick, sir, and — and she couldn't move her hand — not even a speck. I ran and called Nat ———"

"Shoh did, suh!" Nat's loving gaze swept the bewildered boy and as Robert caught something of its comforting warmth, the tension around his heart relaxed. His thinking became less confused, and as though a door had flown open to admit light, he knew what had happened.

In his extremity he caught the doctor's sleeve. "I know now what it was, sir! I know, I *know!*" he cried. "I had my elbow on Annie's hand while we looked at the pictures. It was — I reckon it was a long time I stood that way, sir, because my neck was stiff when I moved it. *That's* what hurt Annie! I know for certain! It was my elbow on her hand that did it!"

His voice had risen to a shrill cry, his slim body shook. Torn between relief at having discovered the cause of his sister's injury and despair at having been that cause, the boy was beside himself with emotional confusion. His mother sensed what was going on in the sensitive young mind, and with all the tact and diplomacy at her command, she tried to divert him.

"It wasn't your fault, dear," she comforted, her arm around his shoulder. "Anne should have realized her hand was being hurt. You both just forgot time. But it was no more your fault than Anne's. It will be a lesson neither of you will soon forget — a lesson in the danger of too deep absorption in *anything*. Now stop grieving so. You know you are my right hand, my 'man of the family,' so you must not give way like a little boy."

The mother's wise words had their effect. Robert squared his shoulders and outwardly at least put the accident behind him. Only temporarily, however. The nerves and muscle in Anne's hand had been seriously damaged and though she was soon up and around again, she grew thin and was subject to grave attacks of nervousness. Mrs. Lee finally arranged to have her visit relatives in Philadelphia and there to be put under the care of a noted nerve specialist.

To Robert her going seemed the final mark of his guilt. Though he never again mentioned the accident, somewhere within the delicately attuned structure of his being a budding capacity for quick laughter faltered and stopped.

So three more years passed. Anne improved slowly and spent much time in Philadelphia. By the time she was pronounced cured she had made many friends there and in Baltimore and was seldom at home. With Carter and Smith both away, and Mildred still the pampered baby of the family, Mrs. Lee turned more and more to Robert for companionship and help.

Courageous Ann Carter Lee was slowly sinking into chronic invalidism. Unhappiness, humiliation, and an unfaltering determination to keep her home and her family secure, gradually had worn away resistence to the illness which now attacked the whole fabric of her life. And to Robert, not yet twelve, fell the duties of a son and daughter as well. A season sharing the schoolroom with cousins at *Eastern View,* his Aunt Elizabeth Carter Randolph's estate in Fauquier County, was soon over. Then he was back in Alexandria, in his heart the memory of country freedom and the knowledge that the need for him at home was great and that there he must remain for the time being at least.

What a strange sight it must have been: a lad ready for school in the morning, tossing books and cap on the hall table while he went first to the kitchen to apportion the day's supplies to the cook; to oversee the contents of the dainty tray being sent up to his mother; to give directions for her carriage at three. Then off to school at Alexandria Academy where Mr. William Leary taught the classics and introduced the boys to Latin and the Romance languages. Home again, and accompanying the dear invalid on her drive, entertaining her with stories about the other boys at school, then settling her on her couch with a book or a bit of sewing while he delved into his home work.

To be sure there were occasional Saturdays when Robert and his chum, Cassius Lee who was also his cousin, would go swimming in the Potomac or rabbit hunting up in the marshes northeast of the town. Or again, there was the museum on the top floor of the market house down on Royal Street where for a modest fee one might see unbelieved wonders from all over the world.

On a windy Saturday morning in March, 1818, Robert and Cassius went racing along Princess Street, bound for home. Time had passed more quickly than they had guessed while they bent over fossil cases at the museum. At the corner they stopped for a drink of water from one of the many corner wells that were a mark of modern elegance of which Alexandria was very proud.

While Robert cranked the windlass Cassius mopped his hot forehead. They were scarcely a block from the Henry Lee house and Cassius let himself hope that perhaps Robert would invite him home for dinner. His own family was away, visiting country relatives. Suddenly he stopped mopping and caught his cousin's arm. "Look, Rob," he said, "isn't that Nat standing at your gate? And isn't he — yes, he's beckoning. Reckon something's wrong?"

The windlass whined as Robert dropped the handle and streaked off toward the beckoning figure down the block.

Nat's dark face was somber and he shook his head as Robert came to a panting halt beside him. "Mas' Rob," he began, his hand reaching out in a protecting gesture toward the boy, "don't you feel too bad, but we got some mighty bad news." Then he saw Robert's anxious glance toward his mother's window and added quickly, "No, Miss Ann she's all right. It's — Mas' Rob, yo' papa, Masa Henry Lee, he — he died. De word jus' came."

His father dead. But how could this be? Why, only a few weeks ago hadn't they read that he was planning to come home to them? Now, so Nat said, he was dead on an island off the Georgia coast. Robert stood staring into space, stunned, incredulous. That he would never again see the gallant, pitiful being who had been his father, this he could not believe. But the kind brown eyes looking steadily back into his gave him his answer. He walked slowly into the house.

From that day forward Robert Lee's responsibilities increased. He must now give thought to some sort of career, a career which would not make too great a demand upon his mother's modest income. In those days young gentlemen of Virginia did not "go into trade." The Church, medicine, farming, law, the army or navy, from these they must make their choice.

The Lee plantations were things of the past; Robert had no aptitude for preaching or diagnosing illnesses; Carter would soon open his law office and Smith was making a career of the navy. There remained the army. Robert had spent most of his rare leisure following his father's death, poring over the fine military library which had been "Light Horse Harry" Lee's pride. Always in the boy's heart there had been a hope that one day he might enter West Point.

Eighteen-nineteen, 1820, 1821, '22 and most of '23 passed while young Lee ground steadily away at his studies. There was almost no time for the rollicking games, the outings and good times enjoyed by most of the boys in his class at the Academy. His eye was on West Point. Small wonder, with so much that was grave crowded into his childhood years, that "young Rob Lee" impressed Mr.

Custis as looking "as harassed as some of our own congressmen."

If sometimes he spent a few weeks at gracious *Shirley* with Carter cousins, clattering up and down its great hanging stairway, galloping along its winding paths, it was never with an entirely free mind. How were things going at home? Though he was never actually aware of it, responsibility rode with him, a feather which weighted his cap.

The year 1823 had had little spring. A bitter winter withdrew suddenly in mid-April and Virginia plummeted into summer heat which played havoc with crops and made city dwelling wretchedly uncomfortable. Mrs. Lee wilted in the heat and early in June Robert took her to *Ravensworth,* the plantation of their distant cousin, William Henry Fitzhugh, about ten miles from Alexandria.

As the Lee carriage drew up before the plantation house, a young girl came out on the portico, hands out-stretched in laughing welcome. "Cousin Ann! Robert! How nice! We've been expecting you since morning!"

She came down the shallow steps and put an arm about Mrs. Lee and kissed her cheek as Robert handed her from the carriage. Across Mrs. Lee's bonnet she smiled at the tall boy and Robert smiled back. "I do declare, it's the hottest June I've ever known," she chattered as they slowly mounted the steps to the shady portico. "Did the drive tire you, Cousin Ann? Mama and Aunt Maria just this very instant went down to the quarters to see somebody who's sick. Uncle Henry's —"

But at that moment 'Uncle Henry' himself emerged from the dim, cool hall, and hurried to meet his guests. Like all the Fitzhughs, he was tall and slight, unmistakably the product of generations of fine breeding. Now as he crossed the portico, smiling his welcome, Robert thought with a surge of affection what a kinsman he was to be proud of, gallant, generous, loving.

"Welcome, welcome to *Ravensworth*," he greeted them, taking Mary's place at Mrs. Lee's side. Then, "Luke — Horace — Ben — here, all of you, come take the bags, and you, Nat, tell th' boys down at th' stable to fix you up with whatever you need for yourself or the horses."

"Yes, suh, thank you, Mas' William, suh." Beaming, Nat clucked to the horses and the carriage circled the drive and disappeared around the house. Nat, like everyone who came there, loved *Ravensworth* and its master and mistress.

So, leaning on Mr. Fitzhugh's arm, Mrs. Lee entered the house and was shown by Mary to her room. There Mrs. Fitzhugh and Mrs. Custis found her when a little later they returned from the quarters. They were all kinswomen, all devoted to one another. Ann Carter Lee was a favorite among the vast clan made up of Carters, Lees, Fitzhughs and Peters, and the three women were soon deep in a round robin of family news.

Meanwhile, in the garden, Mr. Fitzhugh showed Mary and Robert his new hybrid roses and then left them to consult his overseer. If they'd care to walk down to the stables a little later they might, he promised, see a beautiful new colt born just a few hours earlier.

Mary flicked a ladybug from her skirt and stole a glance at her handsome young kinsman. "Brit Peter came over from *Tudor Place* last week," she said. "She'd heard you were preparing for West Point. Are you, Robert?"

Robert looked across the lovely garden patterned by sunshine and late afternoon shadows. "Your Cousin Britannia honors me, Mary," he answered, brows lifted quizzically, a disarming grin tilting his generous mouth. "I didn't think anyone in the whole Tidewater was interested in my notion to make soldiering my career. Since Britannia's heard it, though, I reckon it's no secret. Yes, I'm hoping to get to West Point. There's more to it than just hoping, though. The examinations are mighty stiff and then there's the matter of getting an appointment. If working hard and telling myself I just *can't* fail have anything to do with getting into the Point, I'll make it somehow."

As he spoke, Robert's expression of rueful amusement had changed gradually until with his last word his jaw had set, his heavy brows had come together, his whole body seemed to tense in a crystallization of dogged determination.

Impulsively Mary put her hand on his sleeve. No one, *no one* who longed so for something and was willing to work for it should be thwarted. Her whole impulsive nature rebelled at the thought. "You're sure to get in, Robert," she said. "I know you will. Don't let anything — not anything in the world — discourage you."

Mary's delicate coloring, deepened by the unusual heat of the afternoon, took on an even rosier tint and her blue eyes darkened with the mounting intensity of her feeling. In her frock of white muslin, blue ribbons fluttering from the waist and tiny puffed sleeves, she was a charming picture against the background of the formal garden.

Robert's frank, boyish gaze swept her from the pale ringlets spraying across her forehead to the sandal ribbons that crossed at her ankles, and he made a sudden and bewildering discovery: Mary Custis whom he'd known as long as he could remember, Mary was actually lovely to look at! The discovery staggered him. Mary — Mary — but Mary was just — Mary.

"No," whispered the scented June wind running across the garden, "not 'just Mary' to you any more, Robert. Not from this magic moment forward, though you may not yet realize it."

Robert looked at the slender fingers on his sleeve and quietly put his own bony young hand over them for an instant. "I won't let anything stop me if you tell me not to, Mary," he said gravely and added in a lighter tone, "Come, let's find Cousin William. I want to see that new colt."

The following morning Mary and her mother returned to *Arlington,* their month's visit at *Ravensworth* ended. Robert would remain over the week end to see his own mother happily settled, then he, too, would go back to Alexandria and his studies.

So it was July before he saw Mary Custis again and then

only for a moment following her father's speech on the Fourth. Now, striding homeward, Robert grinned in spite of an annoyance that had come close to ruining the afternoon for him. The grin was a faintly conscience-stricken one: Mr. Custis certainly did love to make speeches, he thought, and such scholarly ones, with so many quotations from the Greek and Latin that it was no wonder the Reverend William Mead had nodded fit to ruin his stock after the first hour in the stifling heat.

Robert's amusement grew as he remembered the good clergyman's helplessly bobbing head. Then he sobered. You didn't laugh at your elders, especially such distinguished people as the Reverend Mr. Mead and Mr. George Washington Parke Custis. And since you couldn't laugh, you naturally gave yourself up to what was annoying you. Plague take that Portia Hodgeson! Giggle, giggle, giggle! Under foot at every turn! Never a split second, what with carrying lemonade and spice drops to the persistent Portia, to say one word to Mary, so sweet, so dear under her bouncing green plumes!

Robert jumped to slap viciously at a low-hanging tree branch. The hot afternoon, the long speech, the disappointment over what was to have been a happy reunion, all combined to form one effectual expletive that came charging up from the boy's heart. "Confound it!" Robert Lee exclaimed and turned doggedly in at his gate.

Chapter III

AN OCTOBER DAY — 1824

M<small>ARY</small> sat up in the big canopied bed and for the fourth time since daybreak looked at the clock on the mantel. Half past six and still raining! Between two windows the black cavern of the fireplace yawned coldly. Shivering, Mary slid down under the covers again, listening to the steady hiss of rain against the panes and the thrashing of tree branches in the autumn gale that whined around the house.

The door leading to the hall opened and a young Negress entered, followed by a little boy whose round brown cheeks dimpled as he carefully shut the door behind him. Abel

44

loved these early morning chores. One day, he boasted to
the other children in the quarters, he was going to be butler
to Miss Mary and wear a blue coat with tails! Now he
stepped softly, carrying his bucket of live coals as though
it were a treasure. Ahead of him, his mother took paper
and light kindling sticks from the deep pockets of her blue
denim apron as she walked swiftly across the room to the
fireplace.

"Good morning, Prissy," a voice hailed her from beneath
a mound of covers as she passed the bed.

"Oh, good mawnin', Miss Mary," the woman
answered in laughing surprise. "Law, I thought you'd be
sleepin' sho' 'nough on a ugly mawnin' like dis. Certain'y
is a bad day, mm, hmm! Abel," turning to the child, "put
yo' bucket close now an' put de coal right where I say, an'
when I say blow, *you blow*. Hear?"

Abel drew his adoring gaze away from the mound of
bedclothes representing his Miss Mary, and gave his undi-
vided attention to his mother.

"Yes'm," he answered solemnly and knelt beside Prissy
on the hearth. Paper and kindling expertly placed, a flip of
the fire pot, a dexterous lifting of a hot coal with the small
hand scoop, then "Blow now, blow ha'hd!" commanded
Prissy. Abel blew.

Yellow flame ran along the paper, licked at the kindling
and set up a soft, satisfied purring. Capably Prissy laid on
logs. "Be warm as toas' in here in a few minutes, Miss
Mary," she said, gathering up surplus paper and wood and

getting to her feet. "Come, Abel, we got two more fiahs to lay before de risin' bell cuts loose."

" 'By, Miss Mary." Abel stumbled ahead of his mother, still casting hopeful glances over his shoulder. And this time he was rewarded.

A pair of merry blue eyes under the lace frill of a night-cap, a wide smile as friendly as his own suddenly flashed on Abel from over the mountain of goose down comforters. "Good-by, Abel," Mary Custis called after the little retreating figure. "You're the very best fire boy in all Virginia. Thank you for my beautiful fire." She waved and ecstatically little Abel waved back.

"Shucks, Miss Mary," laughed Prissy, tossing her head a little with shy pride as she went out and closed the door behind her.

Mary lay looking at the closed door, at the fire patterns beginning to dance on the ceiling, and sighed. Prissy would be back presently with hot water. Meanwhile she could dream. This was to have been such an eventful day, the culmination of an unforgettable week. From babyhood Mary had listened, fascinated, while her father had told about the Marquis de Lafayette, the dimly remembered father of young George Washington de Lafayette; of how, as a young man he had come to the aid of General Washington's discouraged army; of how he had visited at *Mount Vernon,* had planted the lovely magnolia tree while Nelly and Washington Custis had looked on in awe. She had shuddered over his return to France and the terrible Revolution there; of his long imprisonment in Austria. Now he was in America, a guest of the Congress, in Virginia, right here at *Arlington,* in the main guest room *just down the hall!*

General Lafayette he was called now, and how erect, how distinguished he had looked as he stood greeting the guests at his reception on Sunday afternoon. Papa had had General Washington's campaign tent pitched on the lawn and before the tent of his beloved commander the old gentleman had received the homage of the people.

During a lull he had turned to Mary, his thin face wrinkling into a warm smile. "Ah, *Mademoiselle,*" he said, putting his delicate, heavily veined hand on her arm as she stood beside him, "you cannot know what sadly sweet joy it brings to my heart when I look around at you young people of Virginia today. Only yesterday it seems *Monsieur* your father stood, a baby in petticoats, beside me, babbling his baby instructions as I carefully set out the little magnolia tree in the garden at *Mount Vernon.* It was a new garden then, that lovely garden, just as your country was new. Now that baby boy — *regardez, Mademoiselle.*" Lafayette pointed and Mary, following with her eyes, saw her father, gallant, courtly always, bowing over the hand of a little old lady in black. The baby was now a man past his first youth.

She smiled at the guest of honor and he patted her hand. "Another strange happiness I have had in Alexandria," he continued. "During your great war, the American

Revolution, I had a comrade at arms whom I loved as a brother. General Washington esteemed him, ah, very highly. Lee was his name, *Mademoiselle* — we called him 'Light Horse Harry' Lee. Yesterday I paid my respects to his so gracious widow, *Madame* Ann Carter Lee, a very great lady. While I was there I met their youngest son — you know him, *naturellement, Mademoiselle?*"

Mary found her cheeks growing warm. "You mean Robert, General," she answered. "Yes, you see we're distant cousins. We've always known each other."

"Robe-air, mm hm, Robe-air," the old gentleman repeated ruminatingly. "A fine young *gentilhomme*, a worthy son of his father, a great soldier. So, *ma chère Mademoiselle,* the beloved past projects itself into the present through you young people who will carry it on, yes, with honor. That is as it should be, my child, *hein?*"

Without waiting for an answer, he turned to acknowledge the greetings of an approaching group of people and Mary remembered suddenly that her mother expected her to keep a lookout for guests who might be neglected.

She excused herself and progressed slowly from one knot of people to another, graciously assuming the duties of assistant hostess and so like her mother that more than one visitor smilingly reminded another: "Like all the Fitzhugh women, isn't she? a natural hostess, so poised, so charming, exactly like her mother."

Mary had just directed a senator and his wife to the

General's tent when she saw two young men coming toward her. One raised his hat and waved it in gay salutation. "Robert!" Unconsciously she quickened her pace. How nice of him to bring Cassius!

Cassius hailed Mary even before Robert could. "Rob came to boast," he laughed. "You see before you a man of vast importance, Miss Mary, a leader."

"What ever do you mean, Cas?"

Robert came to her rescue as they turned and walked back toward the company around the tent. "He's right, Mary," he confessed, smiling a little sheepishly. "I did come to tell you about something mighty exciting, at least I think it is. I'm going to be a marshal in the parade on Saturday!"

His dark eyes sparkled and his naturally ruddy cheeks were flushed crimson with pride and excitement. Just so, thought Mary, he had looked that afternoon in the garden at *Ravensworth* more than a year ago when he had vowed he would somehow get to West Point. And the appointment had come in the spring — in March. When would he be admitted? Soon, she hoped with all her heart. No one could tell. The list of applicants was long. All this rushed through Mary's mind as she watched him and listened to Cassius's good-natured taunts.

"My friend, General Lee'll be leading a division, Miss Mary. Great leader, the General."

"But Robert, how thrilling! Think of being a marshal in General Lafayette's parade! Let's pray for a beautiful day. D'you suppose you'll wear a uniform? No, of course not. But perhaps one of those sash things with fringes. What do you think, Cas?"

Cassius wasn't sure but suggested something tasteful in ribbons around the head with streamers flying, like a Roman charioteer. So laughing, teasing, they crossed the lawn, three young people who, as Lafayette had said, would carry forward their heritage of high ideals with honor.

A day would come, many years in the future, when Mary, fleeing before an invading army, would look across the shining green lawn of *Arlington* through a blur of tears and recall Cassius's bantering words: "— Great leader, the General."

"Come, Miss Mary, hot wateh — an' look, de sun shinin'!"

Mary came to with a start and threw back the covers. "Oh, lovely, lovely day! Lovely day!" she sang, fumbling for slippers, padding to the window to pull back the heavy curtains. "Prissy, look, just look at that blue, blue sky! Now I can wear the merino dress and my new blue cape!"

Never was a sky bluer than that which canopied the little city of Alexandria on that memorable day in 1824 when the procession honoring the distinguished Frenchman marched up Washington Street. Flag-draped arches had been erected across the broad avenue, the Stars and Stripes and the Tricolor of France fluttered from roof-tops and windows.

The rain-washed air was winey and fresh and carried the sound of martial music with ringing, unmuted clarity to both sides of the river. White-haired veterans of the Revolution stepped off courageously, making a brave show of military precision as they marched along; the State Militia in handsome new uniforms came next; the cavalry troops, proud of their fine mounts and of their own magnificent horsemanship, moved as one. General Lafayette's open carriage had its own mounted Guard of Honor.

Mary, wearing the merino dress and cape the color of the sky itself, stood between her mother and her Aunt Nelly Lewis on a balcony. Beyond Mrs. Lewis, Mary's cousin, Angela Lewis, conversed in sign language with a group of girls on a balcony across the street. Her mother touched her arm.

"Please, dear!"

"But, Mamma," Angela's impish grin always rendered her mother helpless and she flashed it on now, an electric twinkle more than half a century ahead of its day. "I was only telling Catherine Mason that Pappa was in the parade, and she thought I'd said she was to come to *Woodlawn* for Hallow'en, the goose, and . . ."

"Here they come!" The cry went up from the crowds lining the curb. Mary's heart hammered as the first notes of the distant band reached her and far down the avenue she glimpsed the approaching column. Children craned their necks, stepped off the curb into the street and were promptly pulled back to the walk by their elders. Boys

whistled ear-splitting blasts through their fingers and slapped at one anothers' caps in an excess of excitement.

And now the three marshals of the parade came abreast, horses prancing, tossing their fine heads, curvetting as though dancing to the tempo of the military music directly behind them.

Involuntarily Mary leaned forward, eyes shining, lips parted. "Robert!" The exclamation was a whisper but the straight young rider to whom it was directed seemed to have heard. Or possibly his eyes had caught a flutter of a blue cape. Holding his nervous black mount firmly in check, he turned slightly in the saddle. For an instant he looked toward the balcony, his eyes found Mary, his smile matched hers, and with a bow, he swept off his hat.

Angela leaned around her mother to speak. "That Rob Lee had better not be so smart on that fidgety horse of his or the first thing he knows he'll be tossed right smack into the street. And wouldn't that be a pretty sight!"

Mary's laugh at her cousin's sally came straight from a heart fairly singing with happiness. Angela, the darling! At that moment Mary loved the world. That the great Lafayette himself should bow just as ceremoniously from his carriage, or that her father should nod, smiling, from the barouche following it, all this was wholly unimportant to the fair-haired girl on the balcony. Her golden moment, a moment with magic in it, was spent. The rest of the parade passed in a rosy dream.

Chapter IV

MARY AND ROBERT

ROBERT finally was admitted to West Point in the early summer of 1825. Eighteen, eager to begin the career of his choice, deeply grateful to those who had helped make it possible, he was nevertheless uneasy as he leaned on the rail of the Hudson River steamboat that was carrying him to the Point.

The parting with his mother had been painful. Courageous, patient always, the beloved invalid found that giving up the son who over the years had been so unfailingly thoughtful of her, was a sacrifice almost too great to be borne.

She watched as he packed his trunk with the articles prescribed by West Point regulations, saw him at last as he stood before her in his best clothes, carefully brushed and polished, so winsomely good looking with his candid dark eyes and generous mouth, and suddenly the mother's courage failed her. Turning to a neighbor who had come to say good-by to the youngest son, Ann Carter Lee closed her eyes against the tears forcing their way between the lids.

"Oh, how can I live without Robert?" she whispered. "He is both son and daughter to me."

And Robert had heard the whispered words and had wrenched his attention away from the frail figure propped among the pillows. He must not weaken now; she would not want that. So they smiled gallantly at parting and Robert drove off in the stage on the first lap of his journey North. But his heart was heavy. "How can I live without Robert?" sounded in his heart with pendulum regularity, tapped the pavement with every step he took, measured the turn of the steamboat's wheel.

In desperation he searched in his pockets for something to distract him, and at last he found what he was looking for: a closely-written sheet of paper. He unfolded it carefully, bracing it against the river breeze, and read what was written on it. Suddenly his face clouded and he drew in his breath with an audible hiss. A wave of angry color swept up across his face, leaving it crimson from the edge of his collar to the point where the dark hair curved smoothly back from his ears.

How could I! And when it was the most important thing in my life! But here it is before me! Addle-headed fool! (Thus ran the tortured thoughts as Robert continued to stare at the paper, though now self-reproach and dismay were blinding him to everything on it but one word.)

He had spent days in the preparation of the letter accepting his appointment to West Point. Months, even years of dreaming had already gone into the writing of it. The wording had varied very little as copy after copy had been discarded for a fresh one. The penmanship on this one was not good enough; the paragraphing on this left something to be desired; the spacing was bad on another. But finally a copy was finished which seemed as nearly perfect as he could make it, and Robert mailed it, keeping the last draft but one in his wallet. This he knew he would re-read many times, feeling the satisfaction that always follows the doing of anything difficult to the very best of one's ability. Now he read what he had written:

"Sir:

I hereby accept the appointment to the station of a Cadet in the service of the United States, with which I have been honnoured by the President.

The above is the declaration of consent which my letter of appointment instructs me should accompany my acceptance.

I remain with highest respect, Sir,

Your most obliged and most obedient Servant
R. E. Lee

April 1, 1824
To The Honble J. C. Calhoun"

For a moment after he had finished re-reading the letter, Robert Lee stood motionless at the rail, eyes fixed, unseeing, on the wooded shore. The paper rattled in the wind, mockingly it seemed to him, and he was tempted to tear it into small bits and let the breeze have it. Why, he wondered unhappily, hadn't some brain cell pointed out to him that grinning, gloating, wretched, superfluous "n" in the word "honoured?" The letter had been written more than a year ago and had been read many times immediately after the final draft had been mailed. Why, after writing it at least six times, hadn't he noticed his mistake until this moment, a whole year later? A thing like that just could not happen. Yet it had happened and here was the proof.

All these months (the tormenting thought ran on) making a perfect ass of myself; thinking I was pretty smart getting my appointment — Mrs. Lawrence Lewis even going to Washington·to see General Jackson for me; *me, prancing around in the Lafayette parade, thinking what a fine soldier Mary'd think I'd make — and I couldn't even spell!*

Thus Robert berated himself as he was wont to do all his life when he felt he had failed in a duty, however slight the fault might be. That the present mistake was a common one and may, indeed, have passed unnoticed, in no way lessened his chagrin. His heart still torn by the memory of his mother's stricken face when he left her, nervous at finding himself finally approaching the fortress of his dreams, Robert found it hard to keep his lips steady as he folded the accusing paper and slipped it back into his pocket.

The skiff from West Point came alongside, young Lee went down the ladder, jumped aboard the bobbing little boat and within minutes had reported to the Superintendent and been assigned to his quarters. The four years at West Point had begun.

The months passed and the busy years, and the young Virginian made good the promise of fine scholarship with which he had launched his military career. Before he had completed his second year at the Point, his high standing in mathematics won him the position of assistant professor in the subject. True, the salary was only $10.00 a month, but the distinction of having been chosen was in itself compensation enough for the added work the position entailed. And back home, his mother was proud. His enviable scholastic standing brought Robert something which was perhaps closer to his heart than mere cold distinction; it brought him additional furloughs.

Whenever possible, Cadet Lee hurried to Virginia. Mrs.

Lee now was living in Georgetown, District of Columbia, across the Potomac. Not far away was the gracious Peter home, *Tudor Place,* where Mary Custis's cousin, Britannia Peter, kept the big house filled with young friends from "the Virginia side," among them, naturally, her favorite two cousins, Angela Lewis from *Woodlawn* and Mary Custis from *Arlington.* So, calling at almost any of the familiar homes on either side of the river, Robert knew he was sure of seeing Mary. Small wonder then that those furloughs were worth the added effort required to get them.

Meanwhile, Mary was fast becoming a belle. Her keen sense of humor, her fragile, distinguished beauty, the air of distinction and wealth that surrounded her wherever she went, all combined to make Miss Custis of *Arlington* one of the most sought-after young ladies in Washington and Alexandria. Smith Lee, home on furlough from the navy, never failed to call at *Arlington;* Carter Lee, preparing for his bar examinations, found time to write Robert minute descriptions of Mary whenever they chanced to meet, as they did frequently, in Washington drawing rooms.

Mary was blooming. Eighteen, then presently nineteen, accomplished, gay and winsome, she visited at one hospitable Tidewater plantation after another or brought young friends to *Arlington* to enjoy the festivities that overflowed from Washington and Georgetown. Letters came from West Point, carefully worded letters, telling of drills and mathematics and French, and what was she doing to pass the time? Was she well? Answers went back, describing a party at Cousin Mary Goldsborough's and giving a meticulous account of the weather along the Potomac. Thank you, she was well and trusted Robert enjoyed a like abundance of excellent health. Wistful, wishful letters they were, typical of the times, and both Robert and Mary found them quite satisfactory.

One afternoon as Mary sat writing a note to Angela, Mrs. Custis came into the room and stood leaning against the high bed, a half-puzzled, half-amused smile on her lips.

Mary made a little murmuring sound of greeting as she crossed a "t" and turned in her chair to rise. Her mother put a hand on her shoulder and pressed her back. "Sit still, dear," she said. "I'll not be a moment. I thought, though, that you would be interested to know we're having an important guest this afternoon. Mr. Sam Houston is coming over from Washington to see Papa. He'll stay to supper. In his note he said he hoped he would have an opportunity of seeing 'lovely Miss Mary,' — I think that was how he put it."

"Mr. Sam Houston — you mean *Sam Houston, the Congressman from Tennessee, Mama?*" Mary's voice ended on a small squeak of incredulity. "Why, he's — he's sort of old, isn't he? Older even than Carter Lee, I mean? I met him just that one time when Papa took me to hear him debate. Why should Sam Houston want to see me, for mercy's sake? I remember, he was handsome, Mama," she added a little breathlessly as an afterthought, "handsome and — and bold, just the sort of person you could imagine robbing a stage or killing a lion with his bare hands, you know?"

Mrs. Custis's laughter filled the room and she rumpled the soft ringlets that crowned the pretty head beside her. "You funny, funny child," she said. "Pray, what is so strange about Mr. Houston's wanting to see you again? As for his being so old, I believe he's not yet thirty-five. Still, with this handicap of trembling old age, the man's a potential bandit and a killer of wild beasts and, oh, yes, bare handed! Mary, Mary!"

Now they were both helpless with laughter and when Mary could finally speak, she said ruefully, "I know, I know, Mama, I did sound silly, but isn't there something about him — something to do with Indians — if not lions?" Somehow the name of Sam Houston filled her with disquiet, an instinctive antagonism and she dreaded the thought of his coming.

"Yes," Mrs. Custis explained, "Sam Houston lived with the Indians, the Cherokees, I believe, for years. He was adopted by the chief as a matter of fact, and was given a tribal name meaning 'the Raven.' I've heard Papa say he is one of the most colorful figures ever to be in Congress. There's talk of his running for the governorship of Tennessee."

Mary sighed deeply. "Well, I'll wear my bobbinet and try to forget the Indians," she said, "but I still think it's all nonsense, his wanting to see me. Oh, I do recall now! I knew I'd heard *something* about him just recently! Some of the girls at Brit's tea party last week were talking about him and one of them, I don't remember who, said Sam Houston was — what did she say? — was like one of the crusading knights and that someday the history books would be full of him. Did you ever?'' Mary rocked in a fresh gale of giggles.

It was close to supper time, the hour she loved best of the whole day, when Mary went down to the parlor. A fire of birch logs snapped and hissed in the grate and the heavy curtains had been drawn over the big windows, shutting out the penetrating wind sweeping up from the river. Through the archway separating the parlor from the dining room, the supper table sparkled as a servant lit tapers and filled water goblets.

Mary and her mother made a pretty picture as they came down the long room to join the two gentlemen standing before the fire. Mrs. Custis was wearing a gown of soft Burgundy wool, her blond hair piled high in the Grecian manner then in vogue. Mary's frock of cream-colored bobbinet was fashioned like her. mother's and her curls were bound with narrow bands of green velvet to form a Grecian filet.

Sam Houston, deep in conversation with his host, saw Mr. Custis suddenly smile and start forward. He looked up and caught his breath. Enchanting!

"Mrs. Custis — Miss Mary ———.'' He bowed over their hands, but his intensely blue eyes remained fixed in an expression of unabashed admiration on Mary's delicate features and slim young figure. To her annoyance she found her cheeks growing hot and was relieved when supper was announced.

Fascinated in spite of herself, she listened to tales of the Cherokees, of their village life, of their tragedies, their culture. This man Houston with his breezy, informal manner, loved the Indians with a sincerity that was obvious and defended them with every word he uttered about them. Still, there was something rather overpowering in so much and such violent enthusiasm and as the meal progressed, Mary wondered whether her parents, too, were not finding it a little trying.

Now, if only, she thought as she finished her sillabub, *if only* Papa won't ask me to play! But Mary might as well have accepted what was a foregone conclusion. No sooner had they returned to the parlor than Mr. Custis motioned her to the piano.

"Come, Daughter, now let's have a real treat. Mr. Houston," he turned to his guest, "I'm not given to boasting, sir, but if you have any appreciation of music, you are going to enjoy Mary's playing. If I do say so myself, it's fine, fine, sir."

"Oh, Papa, please ——," Mary's cheeks were crimson, her hands clammy as she walked to the piano and sorted the music on the rack. (Oh, why *does* Papa! I feel such a fool! My face is so hot even my eyes burn! I can't see the notes! Now what to play, what to play, what — to — oh, here!)

Mary flipped the pages of a waltz by Strauss-the-elder and struck the opening chord. As she did, her nervousness vanished. Her father had not exaggerated; she played with skill and warmth. There were waltzes, a gavotte, and finally a Beethoven concerto which brought shouts of "Bravo! Bravo!" from the guest and a proud kiss from Washington Custis. And if Mary smiled her wide, sweet smile and if her eyes were shining blue pools as she turned on the piano stool to face her audience, only she knew the reason.

As she played, she had seen a summer afternoon in the garden at *Ravensworth* and had listened to an earnest young voice confiding a life's ambition to her; she was watching a parade and a rider in it as he swept off his hat to her in gallant salutation; and then, more recently, she was seeing a handsome figure in the uniform of a West Point cadet run up the steps of *Arlington* and was hearing again his breathless, happy greeting: "Mary!"

Presently she excused herself and went up to finish her note to Angela. Her mother, looking after her, smiled. This Mary of hers, so appealing in her childlike fragility and artlessness, Mary knew what she wanted of life. A debonair gallant from a frontier state might charm half the belles of Washington, but to Mary Custis he was far less interesting than a quiet lad she had known all her life. Mr. Sam Houston undoubtedly found her exactly the "lovely Miss Mary" he recalled, but there could have been no doubt in his mind when he left *Arlington* that his admiration was not even mildly reciprocated.

Chapter V

A TIME OF WAITING

DURING Robert's final year at West Point he won the most coveted of all the Academy honors, that of being made corps adjutant. At the time of his graduation as an honor student without a single demerit against him during his entire cadetship, his rating was 1966 out of a possible 2000 points and thus he was placed on the list of "distinguished cadets." As such he was permitted to choose the department in which he preferred to serve and Robert asked for a commission in the Engineer Corps.

Graduation was over. At last he was on his way home, perhaps on the same river steamer that had brought him to West Point four years earlier. He was a handsome young soldier, this Second Lieutenant Robert E. Lee. As one fellow cadet put it: "His personal appearance surpassed in manly beauty that of any cadet in the corps." To this might be added the affectionate words of his chum at the Academy, Joe Johnston; "No other youth or man," said Joe, "so united the qualities that win warm friendship and command respect."

Yet with all the success in his work and all this praise ringing in his ears, praise which might have turned the head of another lad of twenty-one, Robert remained the modest, realistic person he had been since childhood. Success he accepted gratefully, humbly, but praise he brushed aside as unmerited. Deeply religious, Robert acknowledged whatever gifts or talents he possessed as coming from God to Whom he gave thanks for them. Not that the young Virginian was a pious prude. By no means; but he was a Christian gentleman in the fullest sense of the word, a man to whom faith in a personal God was as natural as his high sense of honor, an integral part of his being.

With a two-months furlough before him, Robert looked forward with happy anticipation to his homecoming. He had written ahead, telling his mother when he hoped to reach Georgetown. It would seem strange not finding

Annie there. Annie had married Mr. William Louis Marshall, a clergyman, later a judge, three years ago and was living in Baltimore. Possibly Mildred would be at home to welcome him even though, he reflected ruefully, she was more apt to be away, visiting at any one of a dozen plantations, for Mildred at sixteen was no home body.

Eyes on the pennant-shaped path of water as it streamed away in the wake of the river boat, Robert made plans. Recent news of Mrs. Lee's health had been encouraging, so barring the unforseen, he would ride over to *Arlington* the morning he reached home. On the way he would stop and see whether Cassius would join him on a fishing trip up the Potomac later in the week. After that perhaps he would make that book shelf he'd been planning for his room and stain it. Characteristic dreams of a typical young American with a summer vacation in prospect.

Old Georgetown was at its loveliest on the June morning when Robert ran up the steps of his mother's house. Birds twittered in the hedges and the air was sweet with the spicy scent of clove pinks and sweet William. From somewhere in a neighboring garden came the snip-clip-snip of pruning shears and the sound of a bass voice humming in a minor key.

The house door stood open. Robert grinned and took a deep breath of sheer joyous anticipation as he stepped into the cool hall and put down his heavy bag.

"Hello," he called. "Anybody home?"

Silence, broken only by a faint clink of china from the

rear of the house answered him. He walked back through the hall and pushed open the kitchen door.

A tall, gaunt, old Negro, stooped and gray-haired, stood with his back turned, carefully putting dishes on a dresser shelf. The sleeves of his white shirt were rolled above the elbow and, to protect his trousers and waistcoast, he was wearing the invariable dark denim apron of a house servant. With one smooth gesture he could step out of the apron and into the correct blue coat with its brass buttons which Robert noted, smiling, hung from a convenient peg on the wall. No unexpected morning caller would surprise a Lee servant into answering the door in unsuitable dress.

The old man had not heard his visitor enter. He worked slowly, diligently, arranging each dish with meticulous care before taking up another, and Robert noticed with concern that his whole body trembled and that only the drive of an indomitable will kept him at his task.

"Nat ——?" Robert spoke softly.

Nat turned slowly, bracing himself against the dresser, not believing his ears. Then, as recognition dawned on him, a look of overwhelming joy swept across his face. Eyes brimming, arms held out in welcome, he took an unsteady step forward.

"Mas' Rob! Oh, Mas' Rob! Praise God!"

Robert's strong young arms went around the shaking form. "Nat — why, Nat, man alive," he soothed, patting the thin shoulders, "tell me what's wrong. Here," with his toe he wheeled a chair away from the wall and eased the old man into it, "Are you sick, Nat? And where is everyone? Miss Ann? Is she all right? Did she get my letter saying I was coming? Where's Miss Mildred?"

He was patient, squatting on his heels before Nat who continued to sob and rock in an agony of grief. Finally the story came out, brokenly and with prompting from his listener. "Little Miss," Nat's name for Anne Lee Marshall, had been home on a visit. "Miss Ann," Mrs. Lee, had seemed stronger until the hot spell. Then she drooped and "Little Miss" and Miss Mildred thought *Ravensworth* would be cooler, better for her. He, Nat, had driven them all to *Ravensworth* more than a week ago. "Miss Ann" seemed to improve some so yesterday he had brought "Little Miss" back and she had left on the morning stage for Baltimore, less than an hour ago. Miss Mildred had stayed at *Ravensworth*. But now, and the terrible sobs began again, now he knew he would never drive his "Miss Ann" or help her to her chair in the "gyarden" any more because of the sickness that had come on him. And what was Mas' Rob going to do with him now that he was no 'count?

Robert took the gnarled brown hands in his own firm grasp. "*Do* with you, Nat? Why, you dear old silly, get the doctor, of course. But first you're going to your cabin and get into bed. No," as the old man demurred, "don't talk back. Where's Lula? At the store? Well, she can put this kitchen to rights when she comes back. Come, up you go." He drew Nat's arm across his shoulder and with his free arm around the man's waist, half carried, half led him to his cabin in the yard.

It was mid-afternoon before Robert had a moment in which to take stock of the situation and of his strange home-coming. The doctor had come and gone after giving Nat a sedative and leaving him in Lula's care. The faithful old servant, like so many of his race at that time, had been stricken with an obscure form of consumption and though he would partially recover, his working days were over. From this day forward he would receive the same care and consideration that would have been given any sick member of the household. Slavery as such always had been a sensitive spot on the conscience of all well bred Virginians. In the Lee household as well as in the other great homes of Virginia, Negroes were seldom referred to as slaves but as servants, and in the vast majority of cases their good treatment and care was part of the high code of honor governing their masters.

Nat was Mrs. Lee's personal servant, her responsibility. Robert thought of this as he bathed and put on fresh linen. Tomorrow by some means he must get to *Ravensworth* to see his mother. He would send a note to Mary by someone going to "the Virginia side." Old Lula would look after her husband meanwhile, and when he, Robert, returned, he would make some other arrangement. Planning, thinking of ways and means, Robert was not the carefree young lieutenant who only a few hours earlier had come home on what was to have been a happy furlough. "Furlough" and all it implied seemed far away and unimportant now. Mentally he squared his shoulders to take on whatever responsibility might be given him.

Early the following morning he set out for *Ravensworth*, driving the sleek dappled team that had been Nat's pride through so many years. The country roads were powdery with dust and the fields shimmered in the heat; katydids chittered in unison, relaying messages from cornstalk to cotton boll. Virginia — home. An aching sense of loneliness and foreboding settled over Robert as he drove along in the summer solitude. Did people everywhere, he wondered, brushing a rein over a hungry fly that had settled on one horse's back, love their particular part of the country as he did his? Were they as certain as he that somehow the soil of its acres was hallowed? that to die for it if need be would seem logical and right? Thirty years would pass before he would see the bitter answer written large upon the land.

So at last he arrived at *Ravensworth* and went up to the cool, quiet room where Ann Carter Lee mustered her last remnant of strength to greet him smilingly. But Robert, holding the loved mother close, was not deceived. The magnificent spirit shone brighter, more unwaveringly than ever, but its fragile dwelling was shattered. Only a few more days and then those watching beside the bed knew the long vigil was over. Ann Carter Lee was buried at *Ravensworth*.

The death of his mother was a stunning blow to Robert and friends were prompt to do everything possible to divert him. Hospitable homes both inland and along the Virginia waterways were thrown open to both him and his sister, and among these invitations there was one from Mrs. Custis. She and Mary were visiting at *Chatham,* Mrs. Custis's birthplace on the Rappahannock not far from Fredericksburg. They would love to have Robert and Mildred come to them for a week or as much longer as they cared to stay. After all, Mrs. Custis pointed out, *Chatham* like *Ravensworth* was the property of *their* kinsmen as well as hers and Mary's, so why not come to be with their own people for a while?

Mildred, however, went immediately to be with Anne Marshall in Baltimore and Robert was needed in Georgetown to help settle his mother's estate. Afterward, when this was finished, if they still were at *Chatham,* he asked, might he come? Throughout his life, Robert looked back upon the week spent at *Chatham* as a time predestined.

Of the countless beautiful estates scattered across the state of Virginia, *Chatham* stood out, as it does today, as one of the finest. Built in 1750, it had been for decades a favorite meeting place of the wealth and aristocracy of the region. Its crystal chandeliers, its delicately carved cornices and balustrades, its stately gardens and alleys of slim poplars all had had the touch of the Old World laid upon them. To Robert Lee, bewildered and unhappy, it was a bit of heaven.

And here again, as at *Ravensworth,* he was seeing Mary against a background of summer beauty, Mary, gay, sweet, brimming with nonsense and laughter one moment, full of sympathetic understanding the next. Suddenly he knew that any future plans of his which did not include Mary were no plans at all. Yet, he was a young lieutenant with a lieutenant's pay, still awaiting his first orders. Mary Custis was the only daughter of one of the wealthiest landowners in the Tidewater. Did it matter?

*　　　*　　　*　　　*

Moonlight, like a fountain of silver, fell in splashes of light and shadow over a rustic seat that encircled an ancient tree in the garden at *Chatham*. Laughter forgotten, Mary looked up into the grave, boyish face bending over her. How many and many a lover down the ages has asked the same question!

"Not now — I've not the right yet — but when I've proved myself, then may I ask you to be my wife, Mary? And until then, may this be an understanding between us?"

Coquetry was no part of Mary's forthright nature. This was Robert, Robert Lee whom she had loved as long as she could remember. She rose, facing him in the moonlight, and for an instant laid her hands against his breast.

"Yes, Robert, she answered quietly. "I understand. I'll wait — for as long as you want me to."

Mary would wait and Robert would carry with him the memory of her sweet upturned face, of the silver-and-blue tapestry of moonlight against which she stood; of *Chatham's* garden as a hallowed spot.

There were to be two years of waiting for the young people. In August Robert received his orders which read as follows:

"Engineer Order 8

Washington, D. C.
Aug. 11, 1829

Brevet Robert E. Lee . . . by the middle of November report to Major Samuel Babcock of the corps of Engineers for duty at Cockspur Island in the Savannah River, Georgia.

C. Gratiot

Brig. Gen. Commdg."

The young soldier must have gasped. A less attractive spot than Cockspur Island it would have been hard to imagine. True, it was near Savannah where Robert had friends, but the island itself was a bleak, desolate strip of land, storm-swept and marshy. However, orders were orders. Nat could not be left behind; he must, he insisted, go with Mas' Rob. Lula went to "Little Miss" in Baltimore, and when finally the last arrangement was satisfactorily disposed of, Robert and his old friend set out for Savannah.

Nat's ecstatic happiness over the prospects of a journey and of a future to be spent as his young master's body servant was short-lived. Scarcely were they settled in their new quarters when Nat's condition became suddenly worse, and in spite of careful nursing, he died. Sorrowing over the loss of the faithful friend, Robert arranged for his burial and stood, a sole mourner, at the grave-side. With the death of Nat a certain phase of life as Robert understood it seemed to end, the last shred of boyish dependency upon a system of undisputed privilege seemed to evaporate. He was a man now, alone, a soldier under orders from his government.

He soon found that the work of an army engineer was no round of pleasure, but in spite of that, he loved it. Up to his waist in mud and water day after day, the young Virginian labored on the project of building embankments and drainage canals in preparation for the fort to be erected on Cockspur Island at some future time.

After a year he was back home on furlough and Washington Custis was frankly uneasy. Why, worried Mr. Custis over his evening pipe and port, why should Mary have her heart set on this penniless though pleasant (hm, hm, bless me, yes, pleasant) young soldier when half the lads who came calling at *Arlington* had substantial fortunes to offer?

So autumn and another winter passed and in the spring of 1831 Lieutenant Lee, his mission at Cockspur Island completed, was transferred to Fort Monroe at Hampton Roads in Chesapeake Bay. Robert was now well launched on his career as an engineer in the army of the United States. Though far from rich, penniless he certainly was not. He felt he had won the right to ask formally for the hand of Mary Custis.

Chapter VI

LIEUTENANT AND MRS. ROBERT E. LEE

Mrs. Lawrence Lewis stepped from her carriage and ran up the steps of *Arlington* followed by her daughter, Angela. Her cheeks were flushed and the dimples which usually twinkled in them were conspicuously absent. Something had angered Mrs. Lewis and Angela for once was not chattering.

Far out on the lawn Angela caught the flutter of a white dress moving among the shrubs. "There's Mary now, Mamma," she said. "I'll run over and let her know we're here. Aunt Mary's probably around somewhere, too. Meanwhile you and Uncle Parke can have your — er — little chat."

78

Her mother nodded and Angela sped off across the lawn, her big leghorn hat flipping up its brim in front as the wind caught it. A moment later she came to a halt beside Mary Custis who was bending over a newly planted rose cutting.

"Mary, honey ———"

"Angela!" Mary's arms went around her cousin. "This is the nicest thing that's happened in ages. When did you come? Are you alone? Can you stay for a few days?"

Angela's merry laugh went pealing across the lawn as she gave Mary a quick hug. "Oh, but you're a funny one!" she chuckled. "If a lady could possibly be a lawyer — thank goodness, she couldn't — you would be a huge success, Miss Custis. You can ask more questions to the minute than anyone I know! I'll answer those three in order. One: I just this second came — see, yonder goes the carriage. Two: I'm not alone; Mamma's in the house seeing Uncle Parke, and Aunt Mary, too, of course. Three: About staying, I'm not sure. I just tagged along when I found Mamma was coming, so I suppose I'll have to go back when she does."

"Oh, I hope not. Mama's in Alexandria, shopping. She'll be back for dinner, though, and Aunt Nelly'll surely stay for dinner ———"

"It depends." Angela untied her hat and swung it by its ribbons, letting the wind ruffle her hair. She looked suddenly embarrassed. Unwittingly, by her own headlong methods, she had let the conversation get out of hand.

Mary sensed her confusion. "Depends on what, dear?"

The two girls began walking slowly back to the house and Angela spied a four-leaf clover and stopped to pick it before she answered. Then, twirling the clover on its short stem between her fingers, "Well," she began, "Mamma is terribly cross at Uncle Parke for ———"

"Cross at Papa? Why, for goodness' sake?" But even as she asked, Mary knew the answer.

Though Mr. Custis had raised no really serious objections to Mary and Robert's betrothal and had given his consent to their marriage, he viewed it somewhat coolly.

"Plenty of time, hm, hm, plenty of time," he demurred when Mary suggested a date for the wedding. "No need for rushing off like a feather in a gale. Once you're married to a soldier, my child, with never a home place you can call your own, you may wonder why you were so eager to leave your father's house. Mind you, I've nothing whatever against Rob Lee, Mary, but a young lieutenant's pay would scarcely keep you, hm, hm, in bonnets. No rush, my dear, no rush."

And Mary, biting her lips to steady them, made no retort. Mr. Custis, complacent in his attitude, repeated his views to his wife and to his sister. Mrs. Custis's sympathies were equally divided: George Washington Parke Custis, adoring his only child as he did, had hoped to see her married to a man of very substantial means. The mother understood his reluctance over having their daughter enter upon a life that was bound to call for sacrifices and restrictions to which she was wholly unaccustomed. On the other hand, still a young woman herself, she understood her child's heart. Time would tell. Thus reasoned Mary Lee Fitzhugh Custis.

Not so Mrs. Lewis. "Aunt Nelly" loved Mary as she did her own three children, and her brother's complaisance filled her with indignation.

"Parke's calm assumption that he's *always* right annoys me," she sputtered to her husband over the breakfast coffee. "Naturally, he's a dear, but so many of his hoity-toity ideas spring from the same source. He insists on being known as 'the child of *Mount Vernon.*' Well, my word, Lawrence, I was there, too! But Parke chooses to overlook that completely, and now his highhanded manner in dealing with that sweet Mary's romance almost drives me to tears. It's positively Medieval! Times are changing, Lawrence, they really are, and girls today just *will not* be treated as though they weren't of sound mind! Mind you, the time will come when ———." She hesitated, tracing the pattern of the damask breakfast cloth with her finger nail, searching for words. She knew her husband was smiling at her as he always did when she touched on her favorite subject, and was afraid to meet his eyes for fear she would betray herself by smiling, too.

"Let's go back to Parke," she conceded finally. "When we were children I remember how his calm assumption that he was always right used to worry Grandmamma." Mrs. Lewis shook her head reminiscently. "How well I recall the day of Grandpapa's inauguration. Grandmamma and

Parke and I were in an open carriage, driving through the shouting, cheering crowds in New York City. Parke turned to Grandmamma and observed as calmly as you please, 'We're very important, aren't we, Grandmamma?' La, I can see him and hear him as though it had happened yesterday. He was such a serious little boy, so sure of himself.''

"Yes, and I can imagine Aunt Martha's cool reception to a remark like that especially coming from a grandchild of hers." Lawrence Lewis smiled as he recalled the gracious lady who had made *Mount Vernon* the home he most loved to visit.

"I don't recall what Grandmamma said, but her rebukes, so quiet, so gentle, were the sort no child forgot quickly and that little brother of mine hushed. And he must hush now. Those children have a right to their happiness and I'm driving over to *Arlington* this very morning to do something about it. Parke'll listen to me even though he doesn't always listen to sister Mary.''

"Now Nelly, Nelly, my dear," her husband's good-natured laughter followed her as she ran up the stairs to get her bonnet. Angela, coming in from an early ride, stopped in the doorway and looked after her mother's flying figure and then smiled broadly at her father. She had caught the word *"Arlington"* as she crossed the threshold and suspected what was afoot.

Now, walking beside Mary across the sunny lawn at *Arlington,* she was finding it no simple task to answer her

cousin's question: "Cross at Papa? Why, for goodness'
sake?" Mary was deeply devoted to her father and Angela
found herself in the unhappy position of seeming to criticize
his judgment. While she was struggling over a choice of
words, and Mary to tease her, was giving her no help, the
Arlington carriage rolled to a stop before the door and
Mrs. Custis alighted.

She waved to the girls who ran to meet her, and together
they entered the hall just as Mrs. Lewis and Mr. Custis
came out of the parlor. Mrs. Custis embraced her sister-in-
law and gave her husband's arm a wifely pat.

"How nice of you to drive over, Nelly!" she cried.
Then, looking from one to the other, she added, chuckling,
"You two remind me of two cats who'd just settled a dis-
pute over a canary by dividing it equally between them.
I declare, the air's full of feathers!"

Mr. Custis cleared his throat to answer, but his sister
interrupted. "You're a genius at guessing, Mary Lee, but
I'll swoon if I don't soon loosen this bonnet. Lawrence
warned me not to buy it, it's *so* heavy. Let's go up to your
room and I'll explain a small matter of business I came
over to discuss with Parke. We're staying to dinner if we
may?"

Whatever the "small matter of business," it was not
referred to through dinner. Rather there were discussions
of States Rights and tariffs, and of new courses opening
at the University of Virginia down in Charlottesville.
Thomas Jefferson, its founder, had been dead less than

five years; his daughter, his "Patsy," now Mrs. Thomas Mann Randolph and a friend of both Mrs. Custis's and Mrs. Lewis's, was living with a married daughter in Boston.

"Eccentric chap, that Randolph," observed Mr. Custis over his second helping of ham and turnip greens. "Brilliant, dramatic in everything he did, but no planter. The man seemed to have no real ability of any kind. Must have been a blow to Jefferson, considering how much confidence he'd had in Randolph when Patsy married him. And speaking of — this is excellent ham, my dear, excellent. Be sure to give cook a word of praise about it. Speaking of sons-in-law and marriages, it seems to me, hm, hm, Mary Lee, if you women have your hearts set on a June wedding for Mary and Rob, we'd better begin our plans. I'm hoping to do some serious writing this summer — possibly a play — and I can't settle down to it with a wedding virtually hanging over my head. Mary daughter, tell me again, when did you young people plan to have this — er — affair?"

Mary could not believe her ears; Mrs. Lewis and Mrs. Custis studiously avoided each others' eyes and Angela beamed. Thus was Aunt Nelly's "small matter of business" happily completed.

The remaining week in May passed and June came in, the month of roses and bridals. The 30th, a Thursday, was set for the wedding, the ceremony to be performed at eight o'clock in the evening. Now Angela practically lived at *Arlington* for didn't her "dear Mary" need her every instant for help in selecting materials for the trousseau and for deciding on the bridesmaids' gowns? Besides, they must make and re-make the list of attendants many, many times.

At last the 30th arrived and everything was in almost breathless readiness. The tall tapers were lighted in their sconces along the walls; the punch bowl was filled; the last white flower made to hold its head just so on the floral altar that had been erected beneath the arch separating the drawing room and the state dining room.

The bridesmaids, Catherine Mason, Angela Lewis, Julia Calvert, Britannia Peter, Mary Goldsborough, and Marietta Turner, fluttered about the upper hall in their billowy muslin flounces, giggling and whispering while they waited to join the groomsmen below. Robert had chosen as his attendants his brother, Lieutenant Smith Lee, Lieutenant John Kennedy a classmate at West Point, Lieutenant James Chambers, Lieutenant "Dick" Tilghman of Fort Monroe, Lieutenant James Prentiss, and a cousin, Lieutenant Thomas Moore.

It was a handsome company that awaited the bride — and suddenly there she stood, in the doorway on her father's arm. Those who had known Mary Custis from babyhood and never had thought her more than appealingly sweet and fragile, found her beautiful that evening. Never were her eyes so burningly blue; never had the rare, sweet spirit which all her adult life was to set Mary Custis Lee apart, shone with such clarity.

The words were spoken, the blessing bestowed. Lieutenant and Mrs. Robert E. Lee turned to greet their friends. A summer storm earlier in the evening had drenched the gardens and made promenading impossible. But fiddles were tuned, the hall and drawing room were cleared, and two sets formed for the Virginia Reel. The bride and groom did not join in the dance but stood together to receive the good wishes of the older people gathered about them.

Finally the hand shaking, the kissing and being kissed were over as group after group moved on toward the dining room. Mary reached up carefully to touch the tiny knots of orange blossoms caught over each ear, wondering idly when she and Robert might be expected to have some of the wedding supper. Surely it must be almost time to cut the wedding cake. Her gaze, wandering over the big room where the crowds were beginning to thin out a little, settled upon a man sitting straight and alone on a ladder-back chair in a corner, an expression of sheer desperation on his face.

Her lips twitched with amusement but almost instantly she was concerned. Something was wrong. She put her hand on Robert's arm. "Look, Robert," she said in a low voice, "only don't let him know you are looking. Yonder sits poor Mr. Keith, all alone! Did you know he was drenched to the skin coming over from Alexandria and had to get into a suit of Papa's? He . . . ."

Robert stole a quick glance at the dignified rector of Christ Church who had performed the marriage service and then his own face crinkled into a broad grin. "Mr.

Keith in a suit of *Mr. Custis's?*" he repeated incredulously. "Naturally, under his vestments it didn't show, but upon my word, Mary, he's over six feet tall!"

"Exactly. And Papa comes about to his shoulder. Now the poor lamb is out there looking like a picked bird. . . ."

"With his sleeves halfway to his elbows and his trousers looking like slightly long knee breeches and . . ."

"And somehow — I can't understand it — both Mama and Papa have forgotten him in all the excitement and he's wondering miserably how he's going to make a dignified exit. Robert, it's the funniest thing I ever saw, but it's cruel, just cruel! Wait, I've an idea!"

Though Mary was finding it hard not to go into gales of laughter, her practical, womanly tenderheartedness sobered her. "Let's go over to him, then you draw two chairs in a sort of semi-circle, facing him. We'll — we'll surround him. You can bring our plates of supper over there — I'm hungry anyway. Mr. Keith can have supper with us, and when he's ready to leave, we can just surround him again and escort the poor man to Papa's room. His own things will be dry by then, I'm sure. Come, shall we?"

"But how about the cake we're supposed to cut presently with all the formalities?" Robert's eyes were twinkling.

"Oh, my goodness, of course. Well," Mary beamed up at him as a new thought took root and bloomed, "let's go and surround the poor dear with chairs — that much we *can* do. Then we can cut the cake and come back directly and still have our supper with Mr. Keith."

Robert clasped the fingers on his arm and smiled down into the blue eyes so eagerly raised to his. Then he bowed. "Mrs. Lee," he said softly, "I shall always remember that the first request my wife ever made of me was a plea to help a fellow being who was in what old Nat used to call a 'picklement.' Let's go rescue Mr. Keith by all means." He drew Mary's hand through his arm and together they crossed the room.

Chapter VII

FIRST YEARS TOGETHER

"But it's sweet, Robert! I love it!" Mary Custis Lee looked
about their small quarters at grim Fortress Monroe and
smiled up at her handsome young husband. Their luggage
was piled neatly just inside the door. Everything breathed
military orderliness and precision. *Arlington,* its ease, its
happy-go-lucky charm were all part of the past. The present
and the unpredictable future were held within the steel
bounds of army discipline.

Robert untied Mary's bonnet and put it on the chest of
drawers and laid his cheek for a moment against her curls.
"It's not so fine as I wish it might be, dear," he answered,
"but I know Andrew and Harriet Talcott have been plan-

ning all kinds of ways to help us make it look homelike. Those are Harriet's marigolds on the table and Andrew's responsible for the andirons — I recognize them."

Mary leaned her head happily against his shoulder. "Ah, Robert," she said, "Captain Talcott and Cousin Harriet are dear to think of us, but truly, just being here is enough — seeing it, sharing it all with you. Look ———" she broke away to cross to the window — "it's beautiful. You say there are two hundred and eighty acres of island here at Old Point Comfort, but it looks ever so much larger, and all around us dear old Chesapeake Bay. We're going to be *so* happy here, you'll see!"

And happy they were. Andrew Talcott, a native of Connecticut and ten years older than Robert, was his superior officer. He had married beautiful Harriet Randolph Hackley, a distant cousin of Mary's and the four were constantly together. Mary's early struggles with housekeeping in their temporary quarters through the summer and fall months were lightened by the thought that she and Robert would be going home to *Arlington* for Christmas and that on their return to Old Point they would go into permanent quarters of their own.

Christmas came quickly, an unusually cold, snowy Christmas, with *Arlington* servants trotting from dawn to midnight, replenishing fires on the many hearths. The clans gathered; the Washington punch bowl of white porcelain with its gold stars and deep blue banding, was kept filled; the huge front door opened and shut and opened and shut as hourly arrivals from Alexandria and Washington poured in, visitors for an hour or for the entire holiday. The Lewises were there, Aunt Nelly more regally beautiful than ever; and young Lorenzo and Esther Marie Lewis with their baby son from *Audley*. Angela could scarcely wait to confide her engagement to a Mr. Charles Conrad; Mr. Custis read his play and was roundly applauded.

Coming down the stairs with Robert on Christmas Eve to join the company in the drawing room before supper, Mary stopped, her fingers buried in the smilax twining the balustrade.

"What is it, Mim?" Robert used his new pet name as he took her elbow.

Mary held up her finger, "Listen!"

Softly, from the drawing room came the beautiful strains of the best loved of all Christmas carols:

> "Silent night, Holy night
> All is calm. All is bright."

Someone, probably Aunt Nelly, was at the piano and around her, in perfect harmony, the voices of men and women were lifted in praise of the Holy Child.

"Lovely, dear?" Robert found it suddenly hard to speak.

Mary nodded, then: "Let's make it *our* carol for all the Christmases to come," she whispered. "Let's remember it always."

Humming the tune, they continued on down the stairs and joined the others around the piano.

Strangely enough, that first, happy Christmas together was to mark a definite milestone in the lives of Mary and Robert Lee. Following it, their days spent together were at least closely matched by those which separated them. As the January weather was bitter throughout the Chesapeake region, Robert, his leave ended, returned to Fortress Monroe alone, leaving Mary at *Arlington*. There she remained until late spring.

Now Robert's letters were full of descriptions of their new quarters; the garden space that called for her skill with flowers; the large, comfortable parlor; the bedroom with windows "framing Chesapeake Bay." In spite of grinding work and the pleasant company of the Talcotts to cheer him, Robert was growing desperately lonely for his Mary.

In May she arrived, her cheeks pinker, her laughter bubbling, and with her she brought Cassy, her maid, laden with muslin and chintz for curtains and with carefully arranged baskets of cuttings from the *Arlington* gardens.

There followed a busy period for Mary. The new house she found fascinating, and being a well-trained needle-woman, she took pride in the pretty curtains she made and the prim, ruffled "petticoats" with which she covered the many footstools that were an important part of every well-furnished house of the period. Mary, like her mother, was blessed with a "green thumb" and soon her garden was one of the loveliest on the post. Nor did this busy housewife neglect her husband. In a letter to her mother, she wrote:

". . . a coat of his I have darned and new lined the sleeve. You ought to see how nicely it is done."

There was more interesting sewing, too; small, dainty things made of fine linen and silk and the softest white flannel. In September, 1832, Robert Lee held his first-born son, George Washington Custis Lee.

Smiling down at the tiny, wrinkled face, Mary touched the diminutive nose with the tip of her finger. "We're giving you an awfully ponderous name, little man," she whispered, "but to me you're more like a soft, cuddly bunny." So "Bunny" or "Bun" he was to his mother at least, for the rest of his life. When his parents proudly took him to *Arlington* at Christmas time, his grandfather vowed he was "a true Custis" and bending over his crib, reminded him that *Arlington* would one day be his.

At Old Point Comfort — just as at most army posts — life was a round of dinner parties and tea parties and receptions, all of which bored Mary sadly. Keeping her wardrobe neat, and this was particularly hard for Mary since she was not by nature an orderly person, managing her home, caring for her baby, all this was a great strain on the delicate girl accustomed to the easy, sheltered life of *Arlington*. Cassy did her best, but with an inexperienced young mistress to train her, her efforts did not always produce perfect results.

One event, however, set all of Old Point Comfort agog and Mary and her small son played a pleasant part in it. There had been sharp differences between staff officers and officers of the line at Fortress Monroe. So sharp did it become, in fact, that in the summer of 1833 President Andrew Jackson himself arrived to make a formal inspection with General Gratiot, Acting Secretary of War.

Robert knew of their expected visit and when at last the party arrived, he hurried home to notify Mary.

"Of course the President may not call, Mim, but again he may," he said, "so into your best bib and tucker and have Cassy make old Bun handsome." He dropped a kiss on the tip of her nose and was off again, and Mary went up to look over her wardrobe and to stop at the nursery to make sure the baby was napping as he should at this hour.

He was, and later, when the seventh President of the United States entered Lieutenant Lee's quarters he paused, smiling at the rush of baby laughter that floated down from the upstairs. Henry Lee, Robert's half-brother, twenty years his senior, had been appointed United States Consul to Morocco by President Jackson years before and his interest in the younger Lees was deep. That young Mrs. Lee was a great-granddaughter of Martha Washington added color to that interest.

Robert had left him for a moment to call Mary, and as the old gentleman looked about the pretty room with its book-lined walls, its study table on which a work basket and a baby's rattle made claim for space beside writing materials and maps, he nodded sagely to himself. This young Lee was a happy man, he thought, and looking up, had proof of his conviction.

Mary was coming down the stairs, the baby crowing and laughing in her arms. Robert followed, smiling apologetically.

"Mr. President," he said, leading Mary forward, "my wife and my son refuse to be parted or I would present them properly. This is Mary, my wife, and Custis, our first-born."

Mary smiled up at the gaunt, tired-looking old gentleman and impulsively held out her hand as Robert reached to relieve her of the heavy, leaping baby. To the amazement of them all and the touching delight of the President, Custis turned from his father and held out both fat arms to Andrew Jackson. The carefully worded little speech Mary had rehearsed while she dressed was forgotten while Custis contentedly butted his head against the President's cheek and clutched at the stiffly starched points of his stock.

When finally the two new friends were separated and tea was being brought in, both Mary and Robert knew that, whatever the President's opinion of tactics at Fortress Monroe, he found the home life of one of its young engineers a model of domestic harmony.

Soon, however, the Lees were to leave Old Point Comfort. In October, 1834, Robert was transferred to Washington where he was made an assistant to the chief of engineers.

"We'll find a house in Washington and be only a short distance from *Arlington*," Robert sighed happily, rereading General Gratiot's order.

Mary looked up from the little blue coat she was making

for Custis. "Why not live at *Arlington* instead? You know how Mama and Papa would love having us. Papa'd be in a seventh heaven showing Bun off to everyone who came near the place."

Well, why not, indeed? So presently Cassy and her little charge were installed in the *Arlington* nursery and Mary was writing Harriet Talcott about the gardening projects in which she and her mother were engaged.

Meanwhile, though Robert deeply appreciated the fortunate circumstances that had brought such an enviable way of life to him, he was not entirely happy. To Mrs. Custis he gave a son's devotion and had he been her own son she could not have loved him more. Mr. Custis had been completely won over and he and his son-in-law were now the best of friends. Mary and the baby were the center of interest, and life at *Arlington* was ideal. The fact remained, however, that Lieutenant Lee considered his work in Washington largely a matter of marking time, *wasting* time, he sometimes thought a shade bitterly. No wonder then that he gave such painstaking care to the project of installing an innovation in the office of the engineers: a lithographic press.

Scarcely was the installation finished, and as if in answer to Lee's urgent if unspoken wish, when a new and truly exciting mission was presented to him. He was ordered to join his friend Talcott in surveying the boundary line between the state of Ohio and the territory of Michigan where boundary disputes had risen.

Lee set out eagerly, expecting to be back within a month. The entire summer passed, however, before he returned to *Arlington,* to find a baby girl, another Mary, awaiting him and Mary, the young mother, desperately ill. It was spring before she was able to be about again and, after a summer spent at one of the mineral springs, she was quite restored to normal health.

Mary — Mary of the happy, flyaway, carefree nature, Mary was learning how gently, withal how inexorably life bends our will. To be lovely for Robert, this was her one thought always, and his tender devotion and gallantry kept her happily assured that she had succeeded. Then, one day in a mood of loving extravagance, Robert came into her room bearing an oblong jeweler's box which he laid on her lap. He stood back, waiting for her to open it.

"For the loveliest lady in Virginia," he sang out gayly, dropping a kiss on Mary's thin cheek.

They were just back from the springs and though she was quite recovered, she still tired easily. Now her cheeks flushed and her fingers shook as she unwrapped the package. When finally the box was open, a little, wordless sound, half sob, half exclamation of joy, rose to her lips.

On a bed of white satin lay a beautiful comb of heavy, silver filigree. Such a comb a noble Senora would have been proud to fasten in her shining, thick mane.

Poor, blind, loving Robert! Following her illness, Mary's hair had fallen out to a degree that left the sensitive young wife heartsick. Now she held the exquisite comb on the palm of her hand, looking at it helplessly, wanting to laugh hysterically when she thought of attempting to fasten it in her hair, feeling the hot tears rising to spill their infuriating, telltale streams down her cheeks.

"Oh, Robert — it's — I ——" she began, mustering all her self-possession.

For a moment, not understanding at all, he looked at her in bewilderment. What was wrong? What had he done? Then suddenly he knew and his arms went around her, holding her close, the poor head cradled against his cheek; and the silver comb was put back into its box to await a happier day.

Office routine continued to irk Robert and when Andrew Talcott resigned to take up engineering as a private career, he was tempted to tender his own resignation. He was in a rut, a bad one so far as the army was concerned, and felt that unless advancement came soon, he would lose all confidence in himself and in his career in the army. Then, out of a clear sky, Robert E. Lee's opportunity came.

At St. Louis the Mississippi River was churning up an enormous sand bar just opposite the city and another, smaller bar farther downstream. At the same time it was cutting a new source on the Illinois side and St. Louis, left high and dry, lost much of its river traffic and trade.

Wondering who might be best equipped among army engineers to cope with the eccentricities of the temperamental Father of Waters, General Gratiot bethought himself of young Lieutenant Robert E. Lee.

Chapter VIII

THE YEARS BETWEEN

When, in the summer of 1837 Robert E. Lee left *Arlington* for St. Louis — "the West," Mary called it — there was a new baby son, William Henry Fitzhugh Lee, sharing the nursery with five-year-old Custis and little Mary, or "Mee" as she called herself, not quite two. The father must have dreaded leaving his family behind, for the full responsibility of disciplining the children would rest upon Mary; and little Custis was showing signs of true Custis willfulness. For the time being, however, there was no alternative. St. Louis was an outpost city to the far West and Robert felt that until he found suitable quarters for his wife and children, he had no right to expose them to the hazards of an unfamiliar frontier city.

Owing to many disappointments in getting necessary

equipment, he was delayed in starting until mid-summer. Arrived at St. Louis, the methodical young engineer set to work on what was to prove a most difficult and tedious project. By the time all soundings had been taken, maps made and a full report on the work drawn up and sent to General Gratiot, winter had set in.

In freezing weather, work on the river naturally came to a halt and Lieutenant Lee received permission to go home until spring. Impatient over the delay on a project into which he was putting his most concentrated effort, yet eager to be with his family for Christmas, he set out. It was a memorable trip for him because for the first time he was to travel, part of the way at least, by steam train.

By river boat first, since the ice was not yet thick, then by stage, he went as far as Frederick, Maryland. There he boarded one of the "railway carriages" hooked to a small, huge-funneled locomotive of the newly built spur of the Baltimore and Ohio Railroad. Who shall say he had no misgivings? True, on this same Baltimore and Ohio Railroad a steam locomotive had been making the fifteen mile run from Baltimore to Ellicott's Mills, Maryand, since 1831, but travel on the new trains was expensive, somewhat hazardous, and not always so direct as by stage.

The "carriage" Lee boarded was comfortable enough, but by riding out on its roof in one of the seats provided, there certainly was a better opportunity of viewing the scenery as the new invention went puffing and clanging through the countryside. So, in spite of the early winter wind that went sweeping through the Maryland valleys, Lee climbed up beside several other stouthearted souls and they were off, wood smoke blinding and choking them as the little engine gathered speed.

"I suppose," one man observed, clearing his throat, "that if these newfangled contraptions become an established success, they'll find some means of keeping the smoke out of one's eyes and lungs. Peter Cooper seems to have overlooked that feature entirely."

"They may distribute individual smoke screens made of cloth or stout paper — may sell them to you right with your ticket," another volunteered, holding his hat with both hands as he blinked through the clouds that almost rendered him invisible to the others.

Lee did not reply. That the railroad train was no "contraption" but, like the steamboat, a transportation marvel that had come to stay, he did not doubt. As for the individual smoke screens, well, possibly but not probably. His one thought was to reach *Arlington* for Christmas. When the hard-working little engine gave out and was replaced by a horse, he was frankly amused at his own annoyance over the failure of a modern miracle to give a flawless performance when only yesterday its very existence had seemed miraculous enough.

He was at home in plenty of time for Christmas and was discovering how great a period of development six months are in the life of a child. The red and wrinkled little William Henry Fitzhugh he had left in early June was now a lovely

baby, already nicknamed "Rooney," dimpled and pink-cheeked, who went into ecstatic shrieks when his father tickled his chin. Custis, handsome, headstrong, full of questions, appeared older than his five years. Mary, an olive-skinned little girl with a head of dark curls, trotted about on sturdy, fat legs, holding up her arms to her father, murmuring, "Mee, Mee," with the engaging urgency of all two-year-olds who find their place in the nursery usurped by a newcomer.

Little Mee need not have worried. Sitting before the fire with the little girl on his lap, her curls spraying across the rough blue of his coat as she leaned against him in deep contentment, Lee felt his heart would burst with gratitude to his Maker for giving him this tiny girl child for his own.

Mrs. Lee was in better health than she had been for years and sang softly to herself as she walked about the Christmas dinner table, giving it one last quick inspection before having dinner announced. Both Mr. and Mrs. Custis were overjoyed at their son-in-law's return for the holidays, and it was a happy family that sat down to the Christmas feast at *Arlington* that snowy day in 1837.

After dinner as the grownups sat watching the children enjoying their tree, "About railroad travel, Robert," Mr. Custis began, clearing his throat. "I've been reading reports on it, in fact every so often someone drops by who has seen one of the locomotive-drawn, hm, hm, trains in operation or has actually ridden in one. Personally, I'm a conservative about that sort of thing, you know; I like the older, surer methods of doing most things — including travel. But now that you made part of your journey home by train, I'm really interested. Are they noisy things? Do they blow and ring as they roll along? What is it all like?"

His son-in-law thought a moment, trying to recapture his impression of the recent trip. Finally, "Well no, sir," he answered. "I honestly don't think you would consider a steam train noisy. They do rattle, naturally, but that cannot be avoided, and the locomotive itself does keep up a puffing, 'Choo-choo-choo.' Not at all disagreeable, you know, but rather giving an impression of power and strength."

Custis looked up from the picture book he was examining with little Mary. "Choo-choo-choo," he laughed, and his sister, not to be outdone, echoed it softly, "Choo-choo-choo."

Custis dropped the book and began a stamping, shuffling march around the Christmas tree. "Come, Mee, let's play choo-choo train." He nudged her with his toe in passing and obediently she scrambled to her feet and fell into step beside him, puffing busily, "Choo-choo — choo-choo." Thus were these two little children at *Arlington* probably among the first young Americans to use the term and to play the loved game which has been so much a part of American childhood ever since.

Lee spent a busy winter at the office of engineers in Washington, making plans for his return to St. Louis in the spring. And when spring came he did not set out alone.

This time his wife and children went with him. It was late in March when they left *Arlington* and not until June were they located in the pleasant lodgings Robert had found for them in the big frontier city on the Mississippi in the home of a Dr. Beaumont who had three children of his own. Soon the young Lees had made friends and before long they were all so deep in their favorite game of "Steamboat," that their father wrote his friends, the Talcotts, "They fire up so frequently and keep on so heavy a pressure of steam that I am constantly fearing they will burst their boilers."

Late in the summer Lee received his commission as captain of engineers. The next few years were to be trying ones for him. Though he brought every bit of knowledge, every trick of engineering expediency at his command to cope with the navigation problems at hand, the Mississippi River seemed determined to outwit him. Often he was close to despair.

In the spring of 1839, after a year in St. Louis, Mrs. Lee and the children returned to *Arlington*. In June Custis, Mary and Fitzhugh (Rooney) welcomed a new sister, Annie Carter Lee.

Alone and lonely back in St. Louis, Robert Lee worked doggedly on. At Christmas time he was back at *Arlington* and astonished to find little Mary no longer a baby but a little girl of five with tatting-edged pantalettes peeping primly from beneath her full plaid skirt. How the years were flying!

Though happy at being with his family, he was anxious to get back to work. So much still remained to be done. He was now thirty-four years old and he had set himself this task as a measuring stick for his ability as a supervising engineer. That he succeeded beyond his highest hopes was evident from the praise given him by the mayor and the citizens of St. Louis when finally, in 1840, the last of the work was finished. The Father of Waters had been subdued; Captain Lee was now free to go home.

One cloud and one only, had descended on *Arlington* in the ten years since the rainy evening when Mary and Robert had spoken their vows before the Reverend Mr. Keith. It had come suddenly, on a sunny morning when all the world seemed gay. Custis, Mary and Rooney were far out on the lawn, playing with their small, shaggy pony. Baby Annie lay cooing in a big, lace-festooned basket which stood on the portico step beside her nurse who sat knitting, nearby. Mrs. Lee read aloud to her mother. She looked up as a boy from *Woodlawn* came galloping around the curve of the drive.

As he dismounted and handed Mrs. Custis a note, Mary Lee noted the usual happy grin was missing and that the boy's eyes were swollen. She looked at her mother and then quickly at the note thrust into her hand. Suddenly the laughing children, the whole, beautiful, blue-and-gold morning seemed to be swallowed by the black cloud of grief that swept around her. Angela! Dear, merry, chattering Angela, so young, so beloved by her fine hus-

band and her two little boys — Angela was dead. The
first break in the big group of girlhood friends had been
made. Life would go on, of course, but to Mary Lee had
come the knowledge, sudden and without warning, that
Sorrow, the uninvited guest, is no respecter of station or
person, but arrives unbidden and at will.

And time, as it taught, moved forward across the years,
hurrying, or so it seemed to Mary and Robert Lee, from
one project to another with unnecessary speed. Scarcely
had Captain Lee returned from St. Louis when he was sent
to Fort Hamilton in New York Harbor.

There were five children now, the most recent a little
girl, Agnes, born in 1841. Then in the autumn of 1843
Captain Lee held in his arms his namesake, Robert Edward
Lee. Custis now eleven, was sent to Fairfax Institute not
far from *Arlington;* Mrs. Lee taught Rooney his lessons,
and the two older girls, Mary and Annie, lived for a season
at *Arlington* with their grandparents and had their lessons
with a governess.

The five years at Fort Hamilton were to be remembered
by Custis and Rooney as a time of special excitement.
President Tyler arrived in New York on a tour of inspection of the Brooklyn Navy Yards and both boys were
taken to the city to see the parade of welcome. It was
the first big parade either boy had seen and for days it
was their favorite topic of conversation. Again, there was
the smart little boat, *Flash,* in which their father came and
went on his many duties among the fortifications of New

York's vast harbor. Though neither boy ever set foot aboard the little craft, both took a very special pride in it as something which was a definite mark of their father's importance to the port.

Then one spring afternoon as they played along the sea wall, "Look — oooh, look!" Rooney shouted, pointing.

Steaming slowly toward them was a graceful ship, a feather of smoke waving from her single funnel as she nosed carefully through the Narrows.

"No sails, Bun, no sails!" screamed Rooney, his voice breaking into an hysterical puppy-like yelp. He caught his brother's arm and pulled him along the water front after the silently moving ship.

But Custis would not be hurried. "Don't yell so," he admonished with withering calm. "It's only one of the new steam ships from London or England or somewhere. Nothing to alert the whole post about."

"You mean it's the *Sirius* or the *Great Western* that Papa was telling us about?" Little Rooney had abandoned the idea of following the ship to her berth, so instead he climbed up on the sea wall and stood there, beaming down on his brother, his eyes like stars, his whole body taut with excitement.

In spite of himself, Custis caught some of the younger boy's enthusiasm. "Yes, I reckon it's the *Great Western*," he answered. "Papa said most of the steam boats that go across the ocean use sails, too, when the — the — pumps that make the steam break down or something. But not the *Great Western*. She works so well she doesn't need extra help. She hasn't used her sails yet. Look at her go! And take care, Rooney, or you're going to fall straight into th' Bay."

But Rooney capered along the sea wall and presently dropped safely to the gravel path and ran to meet their father who was approaching from his quarters. Custis raced after his brother.

Captain Lee was a strikingly handsome man, well over six feet tall, with dark eyes and raven-black hair. His habitually grave expression and military bearing gave a completely misleading impression of austerity, misleading because one of his characteristics most spoken of by all his children in letters to friends was their father's unfailing gentleness and patience with them. But he never spoiled or indulged them. As his youngest son wrote years later: "I always knew that it was impossible to disobey my father. I felt it in me, I never thought why, but was perfectly sure when he gave an order that it had to be obeyed."

Now the boys went tearing to meet him.

"Papa, d-d-did you see th' s-s-steam boat?" Rooney panted, bringing up with a shower of gravel dust, Custis at his heels.

Captain Lee smiled down at the two excited, faintly grimy little boys and gave Rooney's tie an affectionate twist. "Yes, Son, I saw it. That was the *Great Western* coming in from England," he answered. "They tell me she made the voyage in a day less than three weeks!"

"Wild Indians!" Rooney had just learned the new slang phrase and used it unsparingly. Custis contented himself with a whistle.

"I saw something else, boys," the captain continued. "I saw my friend, Mr. Rooney here, walking on the sea wall. That's dangerous and out of bounds, Son. Remember it, both of you. No more walking or sitting or climbing on the sea wall. Understood, Rooney? Custis?"

"Yes, sir," they answered together.

They walked along happily together in the cool sunshine, the fresh sea wind whipping about them. Their little terrier, Spec, had joined them and he bounced along beside them, barking importantly at the gulls that wheeled overhead, then turning to see how his display of courage had impressed his human friends.

In spite of Rooney's promise regarding the sea wall, his adventuresome spirit carried him from one hazard to another.

In the late autumn of their last year at Fort Hamilton, the usual preparations were being made for the return of the family to *Arlington* for Christmas. Agnes and Rooney were taken over to New York for new coats and hats, and baby Rob had a handsome new, white, fur-trimmed outfit, complete with tiny ear-muffs, in which to greet his grandparents. Trunks were packed and locked; Spec was warned with varying degrees of sternness to "be a good dog while we're gone;" Mrs. Lee gave the begonia cutting she was taking to her mother a final bit of water to keep it fresh on the journey. They were ready. Tomorrow would see them on their way.

Rooney, wandering restlessly about the house in search of something to do, finally went to the barn in hopes of finding some discarded tools. One could always make use of almost anything in the way of a broken tool. Hopefully Rooney poked about. A rimless carriage wheel offered obscure possibilities, but not today; a box of nails, all rusty, and a broken hammer and part of a torn rein suggested several rather complicated inventions. Then, on a hook partially hidden by the hayloft, Rooney spied a chopping knife used for trimming hedges. Eureka!

A few moments later a white-faced little boy marched into the house and gamely held out a bleeding hand for his mother to see. "The knife slipped, Mama," he explained, "and I'm sorry I got blood on my clean shirt." Then he sat down heavily and closed his eyes against the waves of faintness rolling over him.

Rooney had snipped off the ends of two fingers. The trip to *Arlington* for Christmas was cancelled and a very contrite and pain-wracked little boy was put to bed in the care of the post surgeon.

Though the family was divided at Christmas, they were all re-united at *Arlington* shortly after the New Year (1846) and there a little new member, Mildred Childe Lee, joined them in February. Custis was now almost fourteen; Mary twelve; Rooney nine; Annie seven; Agnes four; Robert two and a half, and Mildred the "new baby."

Chapter IX

FIRST WARFARE

"But Mama, I just don't understand!"

Mary shook her dark curls and looked from the pink-and-blue garland she was cross-stitching on her sampler to her mother's face.

A soft May shower was falling and the drenched gardens were sending up a bouquet of heavy perfume. A fat thrush on the lawn shook a spray of raindrops from his coat, turned a speculative eye on the worm he just had tossed on the grass, liked what he saw and broke into a song of delight.

On the portico, sheltered from the downpour, Mrs. Lee and Mary and little Annie sat with their needlework on this spring morning of 1846. Annie's handiwork was a sampler, too, but a very simple one and worked in yarn instead of the silk floss her older sister was using. And the lettering on Annie's was a flower-twined "A. C. L." above the date, "June 18, 1839," her birthdate. Mary's sampler faced the world with the grave statement:

> "Mary Lee is my name,
> America my nation,
> Virginia is my dwelling place
> And Christ is my salvation."

Mrs. Lee was mending a shirt of Custis's but under it, on her lap, lay the letter she had just received from her husband at Fort Hamilton. What he had written only corroborated what everyone said who came over to *Arlington* from Washington. There was trouble in Mexico. War had been declared. Captain Lee had been ordered to go as chief engineer under Major-General John E. Wool.

Mary put down her embroidery frame. "Mama," she repeated, "I don't understand. *Why* must we have war with Mexico?"

The mother's heart may have echoed, "Why, indeed? Why must any nation on earth ever want to war with another?" But philosophizing was not what this eager child wanted. She wanted an answer, direct and unequivocal.

"Because, dear," she answered, "it seems that is the only way the United States can make Mexico understand that the territory of Texas should be one of our states instead of going back to become part of Mexico which it had been until it broke away about eight years ago. The Mexicans think Texas should be Mexican; Americans, especially those who live near the Mexican border, think it should be American. Our government is sending soldiers down there to see that the Mexicans keep to their side of the Rio Grande River and let the people of Texas live in peace as Americans. Does that answer your question, Mary?"

Mary nodded but her brow crinkled in a frown. "M-y-yes. But Papa's an engineer. He won't really and truly fight with guns and sabers and — and things like that, will he, Mama? He'll just make maps of the places they'll fight *in*, won't he? He won't —" Mary's voice was taking on a shrill note of hopeful insistence and her mother shook her head.

"Sh-sh, darling. Not so loud," she admonished. "We must not forget that though Papa is an engineer he is a soldier, too. But we mustn't worry about him. We know he is in God's keeping always, and I'm sure he'll return safely to us. Let's just think of how much he loves us, how brave and fine he is, and one day he'll come marching back to us."

Mrs. Lee had been speaking to Mary but her eyes wandered to little Annie who had been sitting hunched over her work in deep absorption, apparently oblivious of the conversation going on around her. Now as her mother looked, she saw a drop splash on the canvas of the sampler, then another and another. Quietly, with no sound whatever, Annie was crying as though her heart would break. The mother folded her sewing and leaned over to touch the little girl's arm. This hypersensitive child of hers often caused her uneasiness. No little girl of seven should feel so deeply the trials of the world, trials which she could not understand, but which by their very sound implied suffering.

"Darling, what is it?" Mrs. Lee asked gently. "There's nothing to cry about. Tell me."

"I d-d-don't want anybody to sh-shoot my papa," Annie managed to sob, her whole body shaking with the storm of grief that lashed her. "And — and — I — d-d-don't want him to sh-shoot anybody, either. I want him h-h-here with us." A final wave of despair rushed over the little girl and she bowed her head to her arms folded across her knees.

Mary was accustomed to Annie's outbursts. Now she ran a small expert thumb across a flower she just had finished and said in a calming, matter-of-fact tone: "Lots of shooting's just noise, Annie. Besides, Papa knows how to take care of himself and he'd be surprised if he thought we cried when he was away. And anyway, Custis is going to see you crying and call you a you-know-what. So I'd stop."

"Try to remember, dear," her mother said, "that Papa never leaves us without placing us in our Heavenly Father's care. When we think of that, we know neither time nor distance can really separate us because God's love is around us, keeping us safe and together in that love."

Annie's stifled sobs gradually subsided and she obediently blew her nose and dried her tears and picked up her work again.

Captain Lee stopped at *Arlington* only long enough to say good-by. Then he was off to his first war. Behind him were twenty years of concentrated preparation; now, at thirty-nine, he was to be given an opportunity of showing just how much of his peacetime theory he was capable of putting to practical use under fire. He left, confident, sure of himself, eager to do his share in the dangerous work of the engineers who are the proverbial trail breakers in all wars.

The summer and autumn passed and still no fighting as each side maneuvered for better positions. On Christmas Eve, homesick and in a strange land, Robert visualized the festivities at *Arlington* as he wrote to Custis and Rooney:

> " I hope good Santa Claus will fill my Rob's stockings tonight and that Mildred's, Agnes's and Annie's may break down with good things. I do not know what he may have for you and Mary, but if he only leaves for you one half of what I wish, you will want for nothing."

Under Major-General Winfield Scott, Captain Lee participated in the historic battle of Vera Cruz, the most strongly fortified city in all Mexico, which fell to the Americans early in the spring of 1847.

No time now for impatience or restlessness. Lee was ordered from one bombarded area to another, his bravery and the brilliance of his engineering skill giving him an enviable place in the army. In the battle of Chapultepec he was wounded but continued carrying out orders until he fell, exhausted. Scott recognized the magnificent valor and consummate ability of the Virginian and shortly after the end of the Mexican campaign was instrumental in getting for him the promotion to the rank of Colonel.

With characteristic modesty Lee made light of his wound; failed to mention to anyone the many kindnesses he showed frightened Mexican civilians, particularly children; and when General Scott lauded his achievements in the field, he shrugged them off as part of any soldier's duty and so worthy of no special comment.

A year, twenty months passed and then at last the Mexican war was over, Texas was a state in the Union, and Colonel Robert E. Lee came riding back to *Arlington*.

Since dawn the children had been waiting. And of them all, Rob who was five and considered himself the real man of the family since Custis and Rooney both were away at school, Rob was the most impatient.

"My papa will be expecting me to be first of *everybody*," he announced at the breakfast table. "He'll be expecting me to be right at the gate. That's because we're the same — Robert E. Lee — and because I'm a soldier, too."

Mary, now a lovely girl of thirteen, smiled across the table at her serious little brother and then winked at Annie. "You're absolutely right, Robbie," she agreed. "You keep yourself clean and set up headquarters on the portico with Mammy, then the very second you see the carriage coming up the drive, you send scouts behind the lines to let us know. We'll bring up reserves to join you at once. Do you like the idea, General Rob?"

Rob set his silver mug down, methodically licked a moustache of milk from his upper lip, and gravely looked around the table to make sure no one was smiling at him as they so often did. He noted Mary's hand held stiffly at salute, swept the table again for a final check, and lifted his own small, brown hand in response. "Right!" he answered tersely and attacked another biscuit.

Shortly after noon the carriage left for Washington. Soon it should be returning with a sole occupant, Colonel Lee.

Mrs. Lee wore her prettiest frock; the girls, all ruffled and starched and curled, watched the clock; Rob, having exhausted one suit in his morning maneuvers, was now wearing a clean one with his favorite blouse, a blue confection with white, diamond-shaped dots on it, and a final scrubbing had left his round face literally glowing. Again and again he ran to the portico only to return, disappointed.

"It's too early, dear," his mother reminded him for the last time. And at that instant a carriage drew up before the house.

A happy shout went up as the children rushed to the door — to greet with what cordiality they could muster, a friend, Mrs. Lippitt who had come to call, bringing Armistead, her little son, just Rob's age!

The two little boys were on the lawn, absorbed in a game of scouts and Indians, when an officer on horseback rode up the drive, dismounted and ran up the steps.

"Papa!"

"Robert, oh, Robert!"

His arms went around them.

"But where is my little boy?" Colonel Lee questioned, looking anxiously over heads and around furbelows. "Ah, here we are! Here's my Rob! Here's my soldier boy!" He swooped up the little boy who came to a breathless halt in the doorway and gave him a mighty hug just as another lad, his cheeks flaming, his breath coming in gusts, hurled himself at the Colonel.

"*I'm* your little boy! *I'm* Rob!" the late comer shouted as tears of honest rage and frustration welled in his eyes. "I waited and waited and — and ——" this last came in a muffled sob against his fathers ear" — I got Mammy to let me wear my diamond waist and everything — and —"

The others for the moment forgotten, Colonel Lee led the wearer of the "diamond waist" out on the portico and there, in man-to-man fashion, brought peace of mind to him again. No matter *how* faithfully one watched and waited in army maneuvers, he explained, accidents now and then did occur. After all, hadn't he somehow missed the carriage in Washington and come riding home on a borrowed horse? And, speaking of horses, a pretty white mustang pony named Santa Anna, would be arriving any day now! It was coming by sea and would be put ashore at Alexandria. Here was something to which a soldier boy could look forward. Thus with little children as well as with soldiers in the field, Robert E. Lee's gentle tact brought renewed confidence.

That was a happy summer for everyone at *Arlington* and never had it been more beautiful. The yellow rose cutting which Mary Custis had set out the morning so many years ago when Angela had surprised her, was now a mammoth bush, gnarled and heavily weighted with golden perfume. The lawn, kept closely cropped by sheep that moved picturesquely across it, was brilliantly green, the pebbled paths snowy white by contrast. Giant trees formed a perfect background for the house itself. Here was Virginia at its loveliest.

The house swarmed with young people and children as visitors came and went. The mustang arrived in due course, a bedraggled little creature that became fat and sleek and spirited with much loving care, and shared the honors with old Spec as a favorite family pet. Mrs. Lee invested in one of the new sewing machines and taught Mary to use it, and for the rest of the summer the mornings were given over to sewing lessons, with some charming results.

As for Colonel Lee, he was thoroughly enjoying his home and his family. His day's work on the board of engineers in Washington was a welcome respite after two years of warfare; and the evenings were given over to the children and their mother. There was so much to catch up.

So Robert E. Lee and his Mary knew the joy of being together again, surrounded by their children, in the home they both loved. To Father and Mother Custis the cup of happiness they all shared seemed brimming.

Chapter X

SUNSHINE BEFORE THUNDER

THE weather during early June in 1852 had been unusually cool for Baltimore and though the window facing the garden stood open, a fire on the hearth was not uncomfortable.

Mrs. Lee sat at her desk trying to pen a note to her sister-in-law, Mrs. Marshall, inviting her and her distinguished husband, Judge Marshall, to dinner later in the week. But Mary Lee was finding it hard to concentrate on her note.

Possibly the spring sunshine was to blame; again, the fact that Baltimore society had taken the Lees to its heart and was keeping them busier than they ever had been before may have contributed to Mary's restlessness; or perhaps she was uneasy over Custis's lagging interest at West Point. However, in her heart she knew none of these was to blame.

Something was bothering Robert. But what?

For almost four years, since the autumn of 1848, with few breaks in his appointed task, Colonel Lee had been at work on the construction of a fort on Sollers Point Flats in the Potapsco River, below Baltimore. Like everything else he undertook, Robert E. Lee did an admirable job of construction engineering and by the end of 1850 the fort had so far progressed as to call for a name to dignify it. So it became Fort Carroll, named for the last surviving signer of the Declaration of Independence, Charles Carroll, who had died not many years before.

Lee's assignment in Maryland was rewarding in many ways. Not only did he work with a degree of competence that had surpassed anything he had done to date, but his family life seemed to have settled into a pleasant, less complicated design. The children were older and were enjoying new friendships in Baltimore; Mary Lee's health, though never robust, was much improved, and this enabled her to go about more than she had in many years and to entertain frequently in the attractive house they had taken on Madison Avenue.

Her husband was proud of her success as a hostess and tender of her incurable lack of punctuality. At forty-five Mary Custis Lee was a striking looking woman. The fair hair had grown darker with time and was now touched with gray; her eyes had not lost their sparkle nor her smile its warmth. Always indifferent about clothes, she very sensibly put herself in the hands of an adoring maid who loved them. As a result Mrs. Robert E. Lee was one of the most becomingly dressed matrons in Baltimore.

Now sitting at her desk, thinking of her husband, of the possible causes for his worry, she found herself smiling tenderly, remembering the story Mrs. Marshall had told her of that long ago anguish of Robert's when, all unwittingly, he had injured her hand. Dear, sensitive, conscientious Robert who always magnified his shortcomings and underestimated his own worth!

She made a series of dots and dashes on the paper before her, her brows puckered as she thought. Surely the work on Fort Carroll had been a great success — even Robert admitted it was "a nice job" — so that was not the reason for his concern. The children — . The door leading from the kitchen flew open and nine-year-old Rob dashed through the dining room and stopped just inside the sitting room door.

"Mama," he began, making a manly effort to steady his voice, "Mama ——"

Mrs. Lee put down her pen and held out her hand. "Yes, dear? What is it? Come here—your face is like fire, child."

Rob crossed the room to his mother's side, passing a hassock, the tea table, a corner of the sofa like a sleepwalker. "Mama, Spec's lost, he's gone. I've looked everywhere. *He's gone!*" he repeated in a tone of forlorn desperation. His eyes filled.

Mrs. Lee drew him to her and brushed back the moist, dark hair from his forehead. "Spec cannot be lost, Son," she comforted. "He's much too old and too fond of his home to wander far. You'll see, he'll be here in time for supper. '

But Rob refused to be comforted and shook his head. "He's lost or — or something. I know it. He's always at the corner of Mulberry Street waiting for me after school, and he wasn't today."

The front door opened and closed and Colonel Lee came into the room, tossed his cap on the table and stooped to kiss his wife. He put his arm around Rob's shoulder. "And how's my soldier?" he queried, peering into the anxious little face.

Then he, too, heard of old Spec's disappearance and real concern made him grave. Every effort he promised should be made to find Spec. But though he kept his promise, the faithful little playmate was never found and his disappearance saddened the family's last days in Baltimore.

When Rob had left the room, somewhat cheered by his father's promise, Colonel Lee drew a chair beside his wife's and sat down and took her hand in his.

"Mim," he said, smiling quizzically, "I've been in a perfect stew for days, trying to settle something in my own mind." He patted the slender hand in his. "Now the decision has been made for me — rather in spite of me," he added a little sheepishly, "and I can tell you about it. We're leaving Baltimore."

"Oh, Robert, no!" A wave of relief flooded Mary Lee's heart. So this was what had been plaguing him! Now she could afford to laugh in gay surprise. "I hope they're not sending us to the ends of the earth. Baltimore's spoiled me so. Where are we going?"

"Suppose you guess, Mim, just guess." His eyes were laughing now and his voice had a happy ring.

"Oh, but I couldn't possibly. If you've suspected this was coming you've been the most secretive human being I've ever known. Come, tell me!"

"We're going to West Point, dear. I'm to relieve Captain Brewerton there of the command of the post and the superintendency of the Academy."

"Robert Lee, not really! How wonderful! Aren't you proud? Why haven't you told me sooner, dear? I've known you had something on your mind that was bothering you. But why should this perfect, made-to-order transfer bother you?"

Colonel Lee threw back his head and laughed. "Oh, Mim, my beloved paradoxical Mim!" he said. "Made-to-order it is in the truest sense, a ripe and luscious peach on the tree of ambition, but meant for a man of obviously broader experience than I. Why *shouldn't* it worry me? Who am I to get a made-to-order transfer?"

"Oh, what nonsense! There are times when I could shake you, Colonel Lee!"

"But it's true. I wrote General Totten and asked him to re-consider, but this morning I had his answer. He still wants me at the Point. We have until August, so any plans you and the girls have between now and then can remain unchanged."

Mary Lee leaned over and kissed her husband's cheek, her eyes bright with tears of pride and love for this good man whose humility was so honest, so sincere. "Congratulations, my dear," she whispered and could find no more words.

It was September when the Lee family moved, bag and baggage, into their new home high above the Hudson River. The big, rambling, stone house from the day of their arrival held its door open to the endless round of entertaining that went on within its hospitable walls.

Custis was doing very well in his work now; Rooney was preparing for Harvard; while Agnes and Annie visited at *Arlington*, young Mary, seventeen, was the center of much attention when on Saturdays Custis brought friends home for supper. Several horses, among them Santa Anna, had been sent up from *Arlington*, so there were rides along the rocky hill paths and family picnics high on the crags under the autumn sky. Baltimore receded. West Point was home now.

However, Colonel Lee was finding much to cause him uneasiness over conditions at the Point, and these conditions he set about to remedy with all possible speed. Buildings were badly in need of repair; more horses were required for the cavalry and there must be new stables in which to house them. But the most serious lack seemed to be the one hardest to understand in a National Military Academy: this was the lack of discipline among the cadets.

Absolute obedience to orders always had been a point of honor with Lee. It was impossible for him to understand how it could be otherwise. An oath taken, a promise made, this was sacred, and though a man died for it, he did not retract. Now he was learning of cadets who quite casually broke one after another of the strictest rules of the Academy. Not only were these young men undermining the strength and discipline of the army they were pledged to serve, but they were blunting their own capacity for discriminating between right and wrong. They were deliberately damaging their own characters.

Because he loved and understood youth, Colonel Lee was determined to put a quick and definite stop to the insidious thing that was happening to it here before his eyes. That he succeeded beyond his highest hopes and that the severe discipline he imposed still won for him the unanimous loyalty and respect and affection of the cadets must have been deeply satisfying.

One incident he must have cherished developed when two cadets engaged in a fist fight on the parade ground.

One of the boys was apprehended, the other disappeared in the melee and, out of loyalty to a classmate, none of the other cadets would identify him. The following morning the culprit presented himself at the office of the Superintendent, confessed his part in the fight, and asked that he be given his share of the punishment.

Lee looked at the courageous boy and asked him whether he realized how severe the penalty would be. The cadet answered that he did fully, but that notwithstanding, he would know no peace of mind unless he took his share of the discipline.

In the face of so honorable a stand, Lee dismissed the case for both boys with a grave warning and suggested that in the future they try to live in an atmosphere of brotherly love.

Wholly unprepared for such magnanimity, and in an excess of gratitude, the young soldier who had confessed blurted, "That would be easier, sir, if more people were like you."

In the spring of 1853 Mrs. Lee received a letter which filled everyone with misgivings. Mrs. Custis was ill and was asking for her daughter. With all possible speed Mary Custis Lee journeyed to *Arlington,* only to find the beloved mother already gone.

Arlington never would be quite the same, thought Mary as she went about the quiet house, putting things to rights after the funeral. Father Custis would putter over his art files and write his thunderous patriotic speeches; Abel, the

same Abel who had built her morning fire so long ago, would serve the breakfast grits and chicken as usual in his immaculate white coat; there would be twin pink lustre jugs of roses on the parlor mantel, and the friendly sound of carriage wheels on the drive. But Mama, whose gentleness and wit and unfailing thoughtfulness had given the great house its charm, would no longer be there and *Arlington* would be like a garden that has felt the first touch of frost. That its winter should come so soon, Mary Lee had no way of knowing.

Colonel Lee was held by duty at West Point for a week or more, but hurried to *Arlington* as soon as leave could be obtained. Shortly afterward, in writing to a friend of Mrs. Custis's death, he said: "She was to me all a mother could be, and I yield to none in admiration for her character, love for her virtue and veneration for her memory."

The entire Lee clan was shaken by the passing of Mary Lee Fitzhugh Custis. Since Mrs. Lee felt that her father should not be left alone at *Arlington,* she divided her time between her girlhood home and West Point. Thus again the family circle was broken.

Robert E. Lee left West Point in the spring of 1855, left it with a record rich in achievement and there followed two years of the most arduous duty in his military career to date. Two new regiments of cavalry were established and Lee was commissioned Lieutenant Colonel of the new Second Cavalry. This meant severing his connection with the engineer corps, going to the Western Frontier, and being separated from his family. The duty to which he was assigned was the court-martial service and it carried him from Fort Leavenworth, Kansas, to West Point, and back to Texas and the Rio Grande country, with warring Comanche Indians and rattlesnakes for neighbors.

Yet to this man the killing of a savage, even in defense, was profoundly distasteful. As he wrote Mrs. Lee: "It is a distressing state of affairs that requires the application of such treatment; but it is the only corrective they understand."

Camp Cooper, north and west of San Antonio, where Lee had his headquarters for more than a year, was a desolate spot, and withering heat, brackish water and bad food tried the very souls of everyone on the post. In the terrible heat a little child, the son of a young sergeant, sickened and died, and it is significant of the love in which Colonel Lee was held that the parents in their grief, called upon him to read the service at the grave. He complied, his heart wrung with sympathy for the young people whom he knew only slightly, and with longing for his own family.

So a blazing summer moved slowly across the shimmering wastes and in August Lee was transferred to more comfortable quarters in San Antonio. Two months later word came that Father Custis had died. Mary needed her husband. He applied for and obtained leave and immediately set out for home. And a painful homecoming it was, even to a man accustomed to unforseen anxieties.

He had been away for almost two years. During that

time Mary's health had failed alarmingly but, soldier's wife that she was, she had made no mention of her illness in her letters, though to Harriett Talcott she had written: "I almost dread his seeing my crippled condition." Perhaps dear, blind, loving Robert who had given her the heavy silver comb for her shorn head, would still view her tortured, arthritic helplessness through the same rose-colored glasses. So she hoped, waiting for him to come.

Mary Lee was never to suspect the wave of shock and pity that fairly whipped the greeting from Robert's lips as he beheld her gallant progress across the threshold to welcome him. She knew only that she had reached the safe haven of his arms, that somehow all would be well now that Robert had come.

As executor of Mr. Custis's estate, the Colonel found himself facing a situation which by comparison made Indian warfare and the problems of court-martial child's play.

Arlington was in a sad state of decay; the servants, more than fifty of them, as indolent as they were loyal. Debt was casually, hopefully, piled on debt. Distant estates which were under better management, *The White House* on the Pamunkey for one, must help pull the Custis home on the Potomac back to self-supporting independence. This would require unremitting effort-and it would take time, that precious, tragic factor when a man's career just has reached its peak.

Mary and Robert sat late over the paper-strewn table

and when, pain-wracked and exhausted, Mary went to bed, she took comfort from Robert's reassuring: "Try not to worry, dear. I promise you I'll take care of everything."

Yes, she thought, lying in the dark, waiting for sleep, he always had taken care of everything for her. He always would.

Desperately worried over the snarl he had been given to untangle, Robert sat until daybreak, working over the problem. When at last he blew out the lamp he thought he had found a solution.

Chapter XI

THE STORM BREAKS

SOME day war, like the tortures of the Middle Ages, will be considered one of the incredible stupidities of an unenlightened era and will be spoken of with shame.

In the early years of our country the Northern states, held together by their industrial interdependence, attached less importance to the rights and privileges of the individual than did the South. In their thinking and planning they functioned with a more centralized view.

In the South this was not so. The vast majority of early Southerners, and especially those who had settled in Virginia, were land owners whose holdings often covered hundreds or even thousands of acres of field and mountain and timber land. They were a proud people, conservative in their thinking, adherents to the doctrine of States Rights. Added to this, Virginia, as long ago as Revolutionary days, had ceded her enormous North West Territory to the Union that all within that Union might have a share in it. Eventually this land was divided to form Indiana, Illinois, Wisconsin, Michigan, Ohio and a part of Minnesota. Thus Virginia naturally resented the attitude of legislators from the North who felt justified in dictating the rules by which the entire nation should be governed. Among these rules was the abolition of slavery. Tension mounted.

On an October evening in 1859 Robert E. Lee and Mrs. Lee sat before the fire in the family parlor at *Arlington,* discussing Rooney's approaching marriage to his cousin, Charlotte Wickham, when a sealed note was delivered from the War Department. Lee was to report to the Secretary of War without delay.

A fanatical zealot, John Brown, who had been involved in other spectacular protest movements, now headed a slave insurrection at Harpers Ferry, Virginia. Here the government maintained an arsenal. Brown barricaded himself and some of his followers, together with several prominent citizens held as hostages, in the fire house of the arsenal. Robert E. Lee was ordered to Harpers Ferry to kill or capture him; and here Lee showed perfect judgment.

He assigned a company of marines to surround the building occupied by the outlaw band and their captives. Then Lieutenant Stuart, in command, entered to make surrender terms. When Brown refused, the marines rushed in, Brown was captured, and the insurrection was quickly and quietly put down. Brown subsequently was hanged.

To firebrands in the North he became a martyr to Southern feudalism; to Southern hotheads he stood for typical Northern lawlessness. Though sensible people in both the North and South recognized Brown for the irresponsible fanatic he was, the lighted fuse of hatred was now sputtering viciously. In the War Department the name of Robert E. Lee stood out, the name of a skilled tactician who had speedily put down a dangerous insurrection.

Meanwhile, Robert, true to his promise, had "taken care of" *Arlington* so well that it was again harvesting good crops and there was even a modest surplus for needed improvements and repairs.

In February, 1860, he left for San Antonio to take temporary command of the Department of Texas. He must give his full thought now to marauding Indians and to recurrent Mexican border trouble.

In November of that year Abraham Lincoln was elected President of the United States. South Carolina, infuriated at the John Brown incident, had vowed that if an abolitionist — one who supported the abolition of slavery — were elected, it would withdraw from the Union. The time of decision had come. South Carolina seceded; then Mississippi, Florida and Alabama. In February — 1861 — the Southern Confederacy was formally organized in Montgomery and Lee's old West Point friend, Jefferson Davis, was made its President.

Colonel Lee could not believe what was happening. As he read the papers what must have been the thoughts of this gentle, sensitive man with the graying hair and brooding dark eyes?

What had happened to the dreams and ideals of Washington? Jefferson? Madison? It was true that they had differed in their views, many times bitterly, but to dissolve the Union! As well suggest that they demolish their own homes. In a letter to Custis the gravely disturbed father wrote: ". . . I can anticipate no greater calamity for the country than a dissolution of the Union . . . and I am willing to sacrifice everything but honor for its preservation. . . . Secession is nothing but revolution."

Heartsick and bewildered, on the 4th of February Lee opened an order from the War Department instructing him to report to General Scott in Washington. Coming at this time, what could the order mean? Was it war? If that were true, and if Virginia should secede, where would be his first loyalty? Though a soldier of the army of the United States, could he take up arms against his state? Against *Arlington? Ravensworth? Shirley? Chatham?* Against the land he loved more than his life? In simple honesty he knew he could not. Still, the hope persisted, Virginia might not secede. But whether it did or did not, his first allegiance he felt was to his state, his home, and he was bound by his deepest conviction to defend them.

Hurrying back to Washington, he prayed for guidance. In his heart there was no feeling of resentment against the Union, only a deep anger that hotheads on both sides of the conflict had brought such a calamity to pass.

At *Arlington* he found Mary deeply disturbed, for she shared her husband's conviction completely and so did the children. Secession to them was something unthinkable, yet equally horrible was the thought of taking up arms against Virginia.

Virginia Seceded.

Shocked, stunned to momentary apathy, Robert E. Lee on hearing the news went quietly up to his room and closed the door. Alone with his God, he made his choice with what agony of mind one can only surmise. Then he wrote his resignation and sent it by special messenger to Simon Cameron, Secretary of War. The career of Robert E. Lee as an officer in the army of the United States was finished.

His resignation sent, he wrote one of the most difficult letters he ever had been called upon to write, a letter of explanation and farewell to his old friend, General Winfield Scott. This letter read:

"General:

Since my interview with you on the 18th instant, I have felt that I ought no longer to retain my commission in the army. I therefore tender my resignation which I request you will recommend for acceptance. It would have been presented at once, but for the struggle it has cost me to separate myself from a service to which I have devoted all the best years of my life, and all the ability I possessed.

"During the whole of that time — more than a quarter of a century — I have experienced nothing but kindness from my superiors, and the most cordial friendship from my comrades. To no one, General, have I been as much indebted as to yourself for uniform kindness and consideration, and it has always been my ardent desire to meet your approbation. I shall carry to the grave the most grateful recollections of your kind consideration, and your name and fame will always be dear to me.

"Save in defense of my native State I never desire again to draw my sword. Be pleased to accept my earnest wishes for the continuance of your happiness and prosperity, and believe me most truly yours,

R. E. Lee."

To his sister, Mrs. Marshall in Baltimore, his Annie who, with her husband, sided with the Union, he wrote a letter full of love and understanding. Again, it seemed, and in spite of himself, he must hurt this favorite sister, and his heart was heavy when he penned the closing words:

"I know you will blame me; but you must think as kindly of me as you can, and believe that I have endeavored to do what I thought right. . . . May God guard and protect you and yours and shower upon you everlasting blessings, is the prayer of

Your devoted brother,
R. E. Lee"

Within a day he was called to Richmond to confer with Governor John Letcher. The morning of April 22 was cool and sunny and as Colonel Lee stood on the portico waiting for the carriage, his hand in Mary's, the same thought must have struck them both. Her handclasp suddenly tightened, his arm went around her and he drew her close. "When shall we two stand here together again?" the spontaneous gestures seemed to ask. And both Robert and Mary Lee must have sensed the answer. Robert never returned to beautiful *Arlington*.

In Richmond, before the convention sitting at the capitol, he was appointed commander of the military and naval forces of Virginia with the rank of major-general. How optimistic everyone was! Lee was worried by such optimism for he recognized it as simple, honest enthusiasm founded on love of home and a natural certainty of being able to defend that home. To Mary he wrote: "The war may last ten years."

Though the war ended in less than half that time, the four hideous years that dragged their length across the land were so weighted with suffering that, had the conflict continued longer, the price of victory might have become complete demoralization and so no victory at all.

Meanwhile at *Arlington* during the weeks that followed, Mary Lee took stock of the situation, trying to determine a course of action. Robert wrote almost daily from Richmond, urging her to close the place and go to *Ravensworth*. She was, he pointed out, much too close to Washington for safety. Logically, *Arlington* would be the first objective of the Union army as it moved south.

So at last Mary went, but not until the house had been put in perfect order and valuables sent away for safe keeping. Once ready, she left quickly. The girls went with her. Custis and Rooney were preparing to join their father in Richmond.

As the carriage rolled down the drive, Mary Lee closed

her eyes to shut out beloved vistas. Many years would pass before she returned to *Arlington* and then she would be an old woman and no longer its mistress. But later that afternoon, walking with her Aunt Maria Fitzhugh in the rose garden at *Ravensworth,* she knew the futility of trying to turn away from memory. Here, here on this exact spot they had stood, she and Robert, more than thirty years ago. A ladybug had walked along her sash ribbon; a warm wind like today's, had run whispering through the garden; Robert had talked of West Point. Today he commanded the army of Virginia and she was an exile, fleeing before an invading enemy.

Mary Lee indulged in little sentimentality. She was sick, crippled, desperately worried over her husband, her country, but she did not complain. Instead, she set Mary and Annie to winding yarn and gave Agnes and Mildred their first lessons in knitting socks. In just such a spirit had Great-Grandmamma Washington faced the Revolution eighty-five years earlier.

The year passed. The Confederate government moved from Montgomery to Richmond. A man named Albert Pike wrote a gay ballad which appeared in the Natchez *Courier.* Soon every Confederate soldier was singing it, and so popular was the demand for it that copies could not be obtained in Richmond, and Robert had to give up the idea of mailing a copy home. The song was called "Dixie."

The first battle at Manassas was a Southern victory. However, this was followed by several crushing defeats in quick succession and the newspapers of the Confederate states launched a campaign of bitter criticism against Lee that hurt him cruelly. In his many letters home he deplored the apparent failure of the people to recognize the gravity of the situation. For instance, in February (1862) he wrote from Savannah:

> "I have more here than I can do, and more, I fear, than I can well accomplish. It is so very hard to get anything done, and while all wish well and mean well, it is so difficult to get them to act energetically or promptly."

In March of that year Lee was made Commander-in-Chief of the armies of the Confederacy. The outlook continued discouraging as the Union Army, better equipped, larger in numbers, pushed steadily forward. Now Rob, the little "soldier boy," not quite nineteen, enlisted as a private under "Stonewall Jackson."

Through the hot summer of 1862 the war raged on, with battles which have filled the history books turning the beautiful countryside into an inferno of pain and death. Cedar Mountain, Manassas again, Cold Harbor and Antietam — they formed the terrible calendar of destruction. General Lee's hopes rose, sank, rose again. In the midst of the autumn's campaign there occurred one of the major tragedies in the lives of Mary and Robert E. Lee. Sensitive little Annie whose lovely spirit always had seemed reluctant to remain earthbound, died unexpectedly after a short illness.

Lee was brokenhearted and even the great Confederate victory at Fredericksburg in mid-December found him unable to rejoice. On Christmas Day he wrote a long letter to Mary in which he said in part:

> "But what a cruel thing is war; to separate and destroy families and friends, and mar the purest joys and happiness God has granted us in this world; to fill our hearts with hatred instead of love for our neighbors, and to devastate the fair face of this beautiful world!"

It had been at Fredericksburg, while the smoke of battle rolled across the valley that the Commander-in-Chief had looked down upon *Chatham* wrapped in veils of smoke and morning mists. What of its lovely garden? What of a certain rustic seat beneath one of its ancient trees? How much would be spared? How much laid waste?

Next came the battle of Brandy Station and Rooney wounded, later captured — Rooney ever more adventuresome than wise. Then came Chancellorsville, Gettysburg, the Wilderness, Spottsylvania, Petersburg, Appomatox. The years marched on: 1862, 1863, 1864. Then, as April shook out its frail green draperies and moved across the land in that fateful year of 1865, there came to Richmond a rumor and the distant rumble of approaching artillery fire.

The starving, valiant army of Northern Virginia was retreating toward Richmond. Richmond was being evacuated; tattered Confederate banners were trampled in the April mud and brave men cried like children for a lost cause.

Chapter XII

BRIGHT EVENING

LATE afternoon sunlight traced a lacey pattern across the
path leading to the gate and bathed the verandah in warm
September colors. Now and then a leaf disengaged itself
high up in an ancient tree and came zig-zagging earth-
ward with a whispered complaint. Silence hung over the
town, that lovely silence of autumn which is the blending
of many small, drowsy sounds.

Lexington, nestling among the gently rolling farm lands
and forests of western Virginia, was resting after the summer heat. Students were beginning to straggle back for the
opening of Washington College and it was rumored that
at Virginia Military Institute, practically next door, General Custis Lee, eldest son of President Robert E. Lee, would

have the chair of Civil Engineering. A pleasant air of expectancy hung over the pretty college town, a feeling of renewed hope after the years of war.

On the verandah of the President's house, Mary Custis Lee sat in her wheel chair, alternately reading and dozing in the winey air. Robert would be coming any moment now. She must try not to be caught napping. Carefully she adjusted the soft white shawl around her shoulders, straightened the blue enamel locket on its gold chain so that it hung in the exact center of the lace ruffle on her waist and leaned back contentedly and closed her eyes.

What would *Arlington* look like this afternoon? Was anyone remembering to put straw around the rare, delicate plants Mama had tended so carefully for so many years? And what of *Ravensworth?* She had been there only a short time early in her exile. Then had come a "visit" (How blessedly kind every one had been in insisting on calling their generous shelter that!) to *Kinloch,* and from there on to *Audley* with dear Cousin Esther, Lorenzo Lewis's widow. Brave little Esther Marie, a Northerner by birth, had sent her six strapping sons off to war on the side of the South.

There had been such peace at *Audley.* Sometimes, standing beside the delicate sundial which many years before, Nelly Custis herself had placed on its pedestal, Mary felt the presence of the beloved Aunt Nelly to whom she owed so much of her happiness. Almost she could hear the lovely voice: "This too will pass, child. Be brave, be

patient; keep the faith." Aunt Nelly had died back in
1852, a renowned beauty even in her old age.

How full of work the war years were! How fingers flew
with knitting needles, with bandages to be rolled, lint to
be scraped, meager food to be economically prepared, and
now and then a wounded soldier to help nurse back to
health.

That was a strange, unreal period when Mary Custis
Lee found herself at *The White House* where, many,
many years before, dainty little Martha Dandridge had
come as the bride of Daniel Parke Custis. Here, thought
Mary Lee, breathing in the sweet early morning air as she
stood on the verandah before breakfast, here Patsy Dandridge Custis in her scarlet riding habit galloped beside her
husband and reined up beside this very porch, to go running in to one of those bountiful plantation breakfasts. . . .
Ah, all unwittingly Mary had betrayed herself into thinking of bountiful meals. That was not wise, she knew, and
she went quickly indoors.

Her stay at *The White House* was not a long one for
Northern troops under McClellan were moving up and
she must be on her way. On a windy afternoon in late
April, 1861, Mary Lee left, but before she stepped into
the carriage that would carry her to a safer refuge, she
performed the only task she could think of for the safety
of the historic home of her ancestors. With the chill spring
wind whipping her bonnet veil every which way, half
blinding her, she stood before the heavy door of the house,

hammer and nails in her hand. Refusing help, she held a sheet of paper against the door, and in spite of the gale that seemed to be flipping the corners of the paper in exasperated protest, she managed to make it secure. Then stepping back she read what was written on it:

"Northern soldiers who profess to reverence Washington, forebear to desecrate the home of his first married life, the property of his wife, now owned by her descendants.
     A Grand-daughter of Mrs. Washington."

Before the war ended, the historic *White House* was a smoldering heap of ashes.

To Richmond for a time, then to friends in Hanover County through that second winter of the war when Rooney was taken prisoner and Robert E. Lee marched toward Gettysburg. At times so heavy was Mary Lee's heart that she completely forgot her physical suffering. *Arlington,* she learned, had been confiscated by the Federal Government; *Arlington,* so rich in association with everything she held dear, over which Robert had worked so hard that she, Mary, might have peace of mind knowing that it had been "taken care of." It was no longer theirs. Numb with shock, Mary could not grasp the whole truth.

Now back to Richmond and in a little house far too small for comfort. However, physical comfort was of little importance, with the war going steadily, grimly against the Confederacy. At least living in Richmond, the capital, made it possible for Mary and the girls to see Robert often. Custis, who was an aid to President Davis, had his quarters in Richmond, too, so occasionally the Lees held a brief reunion as a family.

Rooney, a prisoner at Fortress Monroe, was much in his mother's heart these days. Charlotte whom he loved so, died at Christmas time, and though Custis volunteered to take his place as hostage if he, Rooney, might be allowed to go to her for forty-eight hours, the request was curtly refused. Yet Mary, torn by grief for her son in his loss, by her own sorrow over Charlotte's death and by deep anger at the harsh refusal, was astonished to find not one word of bitterness in Robert's letter when he heard the news and wrote of it to her. Shamed at her own lack of control, she read:

> "Custis's despatch which I received last night demolished all the hopes in which I had been indulging during the day, of dear Charlotte's recovery. It has pleased God to take from us one exceedingly dear to us, and we must be resigned to His holy will. She, I trust, will enjoy peace and happiness forever, while we must patiently struggle on under all the ills that may be in store for us. . . . I grieve for our lost darling as a father, and my sorrow is heightened by the thought of the anguish her death will cause our dear son and the poignancy it will give to the bars of his prison. May God in His mercy enable him to bear the blow He has so suddenly dealt, and sanctify it to his everlasting happiness!"

Only a great mind, an exalted spirit could have animated so restrained an expression in the face of such flinty discipline. Bitterness was no part of the man who led the undismayed, tattered ranks of the Confederacy toward its eventual surrender just outside Richmond in 1865.

A larger, somewhat more comfortable house had been found on Franklin Street, and here Mrs. Lee and the three girls found there was ample room when in turn "visitors" came to them for the rest and encouragement they never failed to find. Not for an instant did Mary Lee's optimism or courage lag. In a wheel chair, in constant pain, without medicines she needed so desperately, this brave, white-haired woman worked uncomplainingly for the cause she felt was just. But there came a peaceful, cloudless April Sunday when the end seemed to have come to all hoping.

Mary, Agnes and Mildred had all gone to church. Mrs. Lee made her devotions at home. The collect for the day, the Order of the Celebration of the Holy Communion, these she knew by heart and loved. Perhaps, perhaps with so many prayers lifted to heaven, peace would come soon.

Kneeling in their pew at St. Paul's, the three girls, with clasped hands and closed eyes, listened while the beauty of the ancient ritual swept over them: "Come unto me all ye that travail and are heavy laden, and I will refresh you. So God loved the world that He gave His only begotten Son to the end that all . . ." Suddenly, from somewhere in the direction of the river it seemed, there came a thunderous roar as of a cannon. Then another. Startled, the congregation remained kneeling, but here and there a head turned. A messenger stopped at President Davis's pew. The President rose and quietly left the church. The celebrant went on intoning the service.

The Lee girls exchanged glances and Mildred, catching

Mary's eye, soundlessly whispered, "Mama?" But Mary shook her head. Mama, she knew, would rather by far have them kneeling in the Presence of God than running through the streets in aimless panic.

Determinedly they fixed their attention upon the service. Outside, the Sabbath stillness seemed intensified. Once church was over, and the congregation dismissed, the sisters hurried across the few city blocks that separated them from home.

And now where was the Sabbath stillness? The spring sunshine was dimmed by a thin haze of fog, or was it smoke? that hung over the city. Here came a countryman atop his spring wagon, a sunbonnetted wife and brood of children sharing space among the heaped-up featherbeds and cooking kettles with a coop of angrily squawking hens.

"Federals comin', Miss," the farmer shouted, pulling up his team for a moment. "Did ye hear? Richmond's bein' 'vacuated. Lee's surrendered! Best git goin', Miss, 'fore th' towns set 'fire." He clucked to his team and the wagon rattled off.

"I declare, I don't believe it," Mildred panted, running along beside Agnes. Neither of her sisters answered. The sidewalks were becoming crowded now. At every few houses doors flew open and people streamed out, laden with carpetbags and bundles. Nurses carried frightened, crying children; here and there a man staggered along under a heavy chest of silver or an enormous mirror or a family portrait, long cherished. Coachmen brought carriages to a halt at the curb and ran indoors for further instructions.

Impeded by hurrying, jostling crowds, the girls reached home at last, breathless from running and half-weeping with fright and exasperation. But once inside, they found others were there ahead of them. Friends from all over Richmond had hurried to give what help they could to the wife of the beloved Commander-in-Chief.

"Mama," Agnes began with what composure she could muster, "we'll pack and then after you've had your dinner we can leave. Everything ———" she caught the reassuring smile of a neighbor who had arranged for an invalid carriage — "has been carefully planned and there won't be the slightest trouble. Papa wouldn't want you to take unnecessary risks by staying here."

But Mary Custis Lee looked up calmly from the prayer book lying on her lap and shook her head. "I'm staying here in my home," she said quietly. "When your father comes, and I'm sure he will shortly, he'll find me waiting for him. It is the least, the very least I can do for him now."

With that they were forced to be content. Fire, set by the retreating Confederates, swept through the business section of the city, fanned by a high wind; warehouses filled with war supplies must not fall into the hands of General Grant's advancing columns. The air was thick with smoke and flying ash; the streets crowded with people undecided whether to abandon their homes or to stay and see what the morrow would bring. Pandemonium had broken over Richmond as the word, hysterical and premature, was carried: "Lee has surrendered." Another week would pass before, on Palm Sunday, April 9th, the flag of truce was raised at Appomattox Court House and General Lee did in fact surrender to the overwhelming forces of Grant's army.

Meanwhile, when night came on that fateful Sunday, April 2nd, the sky over Richmond was like an inverted copper bowl beneath which the silhouettes of dwellings, trees, and here and there hurrying human figures stood out in black relief. The house on Franklin Street was shuttered and locked. Inside, there was no hysteria, no bravado. Bags were packed, wraps laid conveniently nearby in case of emergency. Otherwise, the day and the interminable night passed quietly. Mrs. Lee in her chair, slept fitfully; Mildred tiptoed from window to window, reporting the progress of the fires as best she could, judging from the glare in the sky; Agnes and Mary alternately talked in undertones or slipped out to the kitchen to cheer the servants huddled there over a pot of strong simmering coffee.

When daylight finally came, the Stars and Stripes, floated over the capitol and soldiers in the blue uniforms of the Union Army moved briskly among the cooling ruins of the city, methodically restoring order. Mary Custis Lee turned her back on the windows. Where was Robert? She wanted Robert. Robert alone could dispel this feeling of hideous unreality.

And at last Robert came, astride Traveller, the faithful

horse that had carried him all through the war; came quietly, wearily, but without bitterness or outward grief. That his cause had been just he never doubted; that all his strategy and the valor of his men had not availed against greater odds he accepted as the will of Almighty God. Though he knew years of hardship and sacrifice lay ahead for the South, there was no note of rancor in his farewell letter to his soldiers or in his words to those who pressed around him in a great surge of loyalty and thinly disguised despair. To his soldiers Lee wrote:

> Headquarters, Army of Northern Virginia,
> April 10, 1865
>
> "After four years of arduous service marked by unsur- passed courage and fortitude, the Army of Northern Virginia has been compelled to yield to overwhelming numbers and resources. I need not tell the survivors of so many hard-fought battles, who have remained steadfast to the last, that I have consented to this result from no distrust of them; but, feeling that valor and devotion could accomplish nothing that could compensate for the loss that would have attended the continuation of the con- test, I have determined to avoid the useless sacrifice of those whose past services have endeared them to their countrymen. By the terms of the agreement, officers and men can return to their homes and remain there until exchanged. You will take with you the satisfaction that proceeds from the consciousness of duty faithfully per- formed; and I earnestly pray that a merciful God will extend to you His blessing and protection. With an increasing admiration of your constancy and devotion to your country, and a grateful remembrance of your kind and generous consideration of myself, I bid you an affectionate farewell.   R. E. Lee, General."

That they all owed allegiance to their country, he warned them they must never forget, and that the quickest and surest cure for sorrow was to be found in taking an active part in helping to wipe out hatred and in setting to work with a will to rebuild what had been destroyed. What spirit! What selfless interest in the land he loved!

And the land repaid him. From every corner of the country and beyond came offers of high positions, beautiful homes, handsome incomes. But these Robert E. Lee could not accept. To live simply, quietly, with his wife and their children for the rest of his life, this was all he asked.

At this time Washington College, renamed Washington and Lee University in 1871, was looking for a new President and when its trustees wrote to General Lee, offering him the office with the very modest salary it entailed, he accepted. Here he would be working with young people whom he loved; Lexington, Virginia, was a pretty, quiet spot, a typical college town, free from ostentation and social ambition. Here was peace.

Thus, old silver and soft carpets and fine curtains came out of hiding; fragile tea cups and dim portraits in oil. Neighbors looked on in affectionate interest while the President's house was made ready; then, before Mary and the girls could arrive, they came with every delicacy known and loved by the Southern householder. On the sunny autumn morning when finally the Lees did arrive, they found a hot breakfast awaiting them, bowls of fall flowers everywhere, the larder filled, the house in order, and new friends on hand to bid them welcome and then tactfully to withdraw.

Seeing it all, savoring its rare quality, Mary slipped her hand into Robert's. "I didn't think I ever could be happy again," she said, her eyes swimming with tears of gratitude, "but after all this I'd be an ingrate not to try."

And happy they were, with the girls entering into the social life of the little town, with Rooney blissfully re-married, with Custis settled in his work at the Virginia Military Institute and college life flowing through the house like the warm, steady pulse of youth itself.

*   *   *   *

President Lee walked slowly up the path to the house. Coming home was always so pleasant, so restful after a full day in the college office. There would be time for a nap before supper and afterward there would be young people calling and music and laughter. He climbed the steps of the verandah before he was aware of Mary's chair, standing slightly at an angle in a sheltered corner.

He smiled. Bless her heart, she'd dozed off. He drew up a chair and sat down beside her, thinking how little, how very little time had changed this Mary of his. Once long ago, he mused, watching the shadows, there'd been some sort of celebration somewhere and she'd worn a perky little hat with a bobbing feather on it. Another girl, a great gig-gler named Portia somebody, had monopolized all his time. He remembered racing home, slapping at tree branches and gate posts in an excess of irritation.

Long ago that had been — long ago. He took off his soft hat and ran his fingers through his thick white hair. Where had time gone? A seed pod drifted lazily down across the verandah and settled its tiny puff on Mary's hand where it rested in her lap. Robert laid his own hand gently over hers.

She stirred, opened her eyes. "Ah, but I'm a zaney," she apologized, smiling up at him. "There I go, drifting off to sleep when all the time I've been planning how very fine I wanted to look when you came!"

"The nap did you far more good, dear," her husband answered. "As for looking fine for my home coming, I cannot remember the time when you didn't. You've spoiled me badly, Mim, badly."

Hands entwined, they sat looking out into the golden haze of approaching twilight. Four more years and then the great spirit of Robert E. Lee would be called, to be followed three years later by that of "Mim" who could not long be happy without him. Now, far from *Arlington* and the era of luxury for which it stood, these two knew a peace and serenity far above personal love, hate, political animosity or pride. To the past they had given freely and joyously of themselves; the present held their loyalty and love for the college to which Robert was directing the finest instructional work of his long career. But to the future, to those who had known and remembered and loved Mary and Robert from childhood, they would be simply the Lees of *Arlington*.